MASTERS

of the

OCEANS

MASTERS
of the
OCEANS

WHALES • DOLPHINS • SHARKS

MICHAEL BRIGHT

First published in the United Kingdom 1991 by
PRION,
an imprint of Multimedia Books Limited,
32 - 34 Gordon House Road, London NW5 1LP

Text and compilation copyright © Multimedia Books Limited 1991

Editor Anne Cope
Design and typesetting Kelly Maskall
Production Hugh Allan

British Library Cataloguing-in-Publication Data
Bright, Michael
    Masters of the oceans: Whales, dolphins and sharks
    I. Title
    599.5

    ISBN 1-85375-073-5

Printed in Singapore by Imago

10 9 8 7 6 5 4 3 2

CONTENTS

Beluga whales in the Barrow Strait, between Cornwallis Island and Prince of Wales Island in the Canadian Arctic. By thrashing around in the gravelly shallows, the whales clean off the dirty yellow coating of diatoms that accumulates on their skin during the rest of the year. Beluga herds can number up to 1,200 individuals.

Whales, dolphins, and sharks are some of the sea's most impressive creatures. Who can fail to be excited by the sight of a gigantic baleen whale leaping clear of the water, or amused by a school of wave-riding dolphins, or awed by the ferocity of an attacking shark?

There are 10 species of baleen whales, 68 known species of toothed whales – including orcas, dolphins, and the sperm whale – and 368 recognized species of sharks, and new species are being discovered all the time. Some small whales, beaked whales for example, are known only from a few carcasses washed ashore. No one has ever seen them alive. Other exotics, such as the high-finned sperm whale seen off the Shetland Islands or the black-and-white spotted dolphin with a twin dorsal fin seen in the Mediterranean, have been glimpsed so briefly that science has not yet given them official names.

Some giant sea creatures turn up quite literally 'out of the blue'. In 1976 an unknown species of giant deepsea shark, dubbed 'megamouth' on account of its enormous gape, became fouled in a sea anchor off Hawaii. Since then several of these 15-foot (4.6-meter) sharks have been washed ashore or caught in nets. In 1990, off the coast of California, a living specimen was filmed as it was released back into deep water.

Top of the food chain

Many whales, dolphins, and sharks are 'apex predators'– they are right at the top of their respective food chains. The tiger shark, which can grow to 20 feet (6.1 meters) and weigh more than 3,000 pounds (1,360 kg), is at the summit of a complex pyramid of life and death. At the base of the pyramid are enormous numbers of simple organisms; higher up, the species become fewer in number but more complicated in their structure and behavior; at the top of the pyramid sit the sophisticated predators. For example, microscopic plants (phytoplankton) are eaten by microscopic animals (zooplankton), which are scooped up by small fishes, which are caught by larger fishes, which are eaten by tiger sharks (which have also been known to attack car tires!).

Some apex predators skip a link or two in the chain. The giant baleen whales, for example, the largest creatures that have ever lived on earth – the blue whale can be 100 feet (30 meters) long and weigh up to 140 tons – feed on tiny floating shrimps and fishes.

Apex predators have few enemies – few animals which eat them – and they include some of the most efficient killers in the sea. The great white shark, the largest of all predatory fish, was brought to world attention in Peter Benchley's popular book *Jaws* and in the many films that followed. The shark in the film was outsize, larger than life, but then real great whites are pretty impressive, up to 30 feet (9.0 meters) in length. A shark of that size has jaws that can exert a biting force of 50 tons per square inch (8.5 tonnes/cm^2) and take a 30-inch (76-cm) chunk out of its prey.

Herman Melville chose the largest carnivore in the sea, a male sperm whale, for his novel *Moby Dick*. The 'great white whale' that haunted and finally destroyed Captain Ahab may well have been 80 feet (24.5 meters) long, but today the average for sperm whales is nearer 50 feet (15 meters), which corresponds to a weight of 36 tons. The teeth in the lower jaw of a bull sperm whale can be up to 11 inches (28 cm) long and weigh up to 4 pounds (1.8 kg) each. Sperm whales dive deep, into the abyssal darkness, in their search for giant squid,

locating them with high-frequency echolocation clicks. A giant squid, or kraken, has a streamlined body 10 feet (3 meters) long and 20-foot (6-meter) tentacles, a worthy adversary for a whale the size of a bus. Huge sucker marks, 6 inches (10 cm) across, on the head of many sperm whales bear witness to such undersea dramas.

And then there is the infamous orca, or killer whale, the largest, fastest, and most powerful of the dolphins. The Romans named it after the king of the Underworld; the Germans call it the 'sword-whale', a reference to the tall sword-like dorsal fin of the male; the Scandinavians know it as the 'blubber-chopper' and the Spanish as the 'assassin'. The orca is the only whale that hunts warm-blooded prey.

Exploiters exploited

All of these remarkable creatures have, over millions of years of evolutionary trial and error, become supreme predators. Yet, despite their size and their power, they are among the most vulnerable creatures on the planet, vulnerable, that is, to the activities of that ultimate predator, man.

The whaling industry brought many species of whales to the edge of extinction. Stocks were exploited indiscriminately, without a thought for the future. Whaling was a 'boom and bust' business. The largest whales disappeared first, followed by progressively smaller species. In the end, very few were left.

Today, even the friendly dolphin is being hit. In the Black Sea, thousands of dolphins have been slaughtered for their oil. On certain Japanese islands, schools of dolphins are herded onto beaches, killed, and ground up into animal feed. Other dolphins are the innocent victims of the gigantic purse-seine nets used by the tuna fishing industry.

View of LOCH-RANZA BAY *in* SCOTLAND *with the manner of taking the Basking Shark*

A great basking shark being taken in Lochranza Bay off the Isle of Arran, Scotland. Basking sharks live in temperate waters and grow to a length of about 35 feet (11 meters). They are sluggish swimmers and feed on plankton at the sea's surface. The body is stout, and the gill slits start almost on the top of the head and extend right round to the throat.

Right: A great sperm whale lies hauled up on an Icelandic flensing platform. The bulbous forehead contains spermaceti, a waxy substance that gives the whale negative buoyancy when it dives down to the depths, and positive buoyancy when it comes up again, thus saving considerable energy. Sperm whales are thought to dive to depths of 1 ½ miles (2.5 km) or more.

9

And now the same thing is happening to sharks. The basking shark, hunted for the oil in its liver, has all but disappeared from the northeastern Atlantic. The oil was used to lubricate precision machinery and to ensure that high-altitude aircraft continued to function properly. Then shark liver oil was found to be very similar to the oils in human skin. In recent years, millions of deepwater sharks have perished for the sake of face creams.

Vanity of a different kind threatens the great white and other large sharks. Macho sports fishermen, exorcising the human fear of being eaten alive, take revenge on sharks. Catching and landing a giant shark is the ultimate status symbol among sports fishermen. The consequences, for the sharks, have been disastrous. In parts of South Australia, the great white is probably dying out. Giant females are no longer seen; they have been fished out. Only smaller males put in an appearance, attracted by the 'chum slicks' of a new breed of intrepid explorer, the scuba diver who wants to come face to face with a great white, preferably from inside a safety cage. All the really large great whites have succumbed to the ambitions of 'sports' fishermen,

who nail the excised jaws to their living-room walls to impress the neighbors.

Shark fin soup has also become big business. Demand for shark fins is so great that some fishermen on the East Coast of the United States cut off the fins and throw the still-living bodies back into the sea. A de-finned tiger shark was found wallowing on the seabed, unable to move. Where sharks are concerned, human cruelty seems to know no bounds.

There is a terrible price to pay for this uncontrolled exploitation. Top predators are slow to reproduce. There are always fewer predators than prey, they have fewer offspring, and they reproduce less often. When a predator population is hit, it is slow to recover. A pause in commercial whaling has meant the gradual return of the giant baleen whales. Even so, blue, fin, bowhead, right, and humpback whales are still considered to be endangered, and the pressure from some countries to re-start commercial whaling has conservationists very worried indeed.

There are few controls over shark fishing and sharks

Above: The blowhole of a fin whale, the second largest of the great whales after the blue whale.

Above right: The spout of a blue whale. There are separate populations of blue whales in both hemispheres, with those in the Southern Hemisphere tending to grow larger (up to 98 ft/30 meters).

have few supporters. They don't have the gentle nature of a humpback or the winning smile of a bottlenose dolphin. They have been labeled 'killers' and killers they will always be, and so, human nature being what it is, we shall continue to destroy a group of animals that has survived on this planet for hundreds of millions of years.

Evolution and adaptation

Sharks evolved many earth ages before whales or dolphins. Ancient relatives of modern sharks hunted the oceans of 400 million years ago. Fossil shark teeth have been found embedded in rocks laid down in the Late Middle Devonian period, 380 million years ago. Whales and dolphins did not evolve until much later, in the Middle Eocene, about 50 million years ago. As they evolved, they lost the hind limbs and the mobile neck of their land-living ancestors, but gained steerable flippers and a propulsive tail.

Sharks are fishes and have always lived in the sea. They absorb oxygen from the water passing through their gills. Some species must be continually on the move in order to ensure a flow of water through the gills. Others have the ability to pump water through their gill chambers by tensing the floor of the mouth.

Whales and dolphins are mammals and have to come up to the surface to breathe, so the nostrils have moved from the front to the top of the head, where they open as a blowhole. The larger baleen whales can be recognized by the shape of the spout they blow to the clear the stale air out of their lungs before taking another breath. The 'spout', or 'blow', of a gray whale is vertical, a right whale has two distinct jets in a vertical cone, and the sperm whale directs its jet forward at an angle of 45 degrees. Blue whales throw up a spout 30 feet (10 meters) high.

Interestingly, dolphins and sharks, although separated by 350 million years of evolution, have roughly the same body shape. Icthyosaurs, the ancient swimming relatives of the dinosaurs, also had a similar shape. The process of arriving at a similar solution from different points of departure is known as 'convergent evolution'. Sharks, ichthyosaurs, and dolphins have a streamlined, torpedo-shaped body, an erect stiff triangular dorsal fin, and a powerful propulsive tail. There the similarities end, however. Whereas sharks and icthyosaurs propel themselves with side-to-side

Above: A humpback whale blowing. Like the blue whale and fin whale, humpbacks are baleen whales and graze on krill and other plankton which they sieve through the baleen bristles growing from their upper jaw. The knobbly profile is typical of the species.

Right: A whale shark caught off Sydney harbor in Australia. Boats have been known to ram whale sharks, which have a habit of sleeping at the surface of the sea. From snout to tail tip, this specimen measured 56 feet (17 meters). Whale sharks feed on plankton and are not at all dangerous.

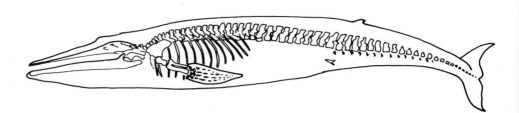

Above: With no need for support against gravity, whales and dolphins have dispensed with hind limbs and their forelimbs have been reduced to paddles. The main component of a whale's or dolphin's skeleton is the backbone, for the attachment of the massive blocks of muscle that move the tail.

But sometimes evolution takes a backward step: a humpback was once caught which had hind legs about 3 feet (1 meter) long! The odds of such a gene persisting through nearly 50 million years are vanishingly small.

Fossils of primitive whales have been found in Pakistan, not among the bones of deepsea creatures but among those of crocodiles, turtles, catfish, and other estuary dwellers. Palaeontologists believe that whales are descended from a wolf-like ancestor.

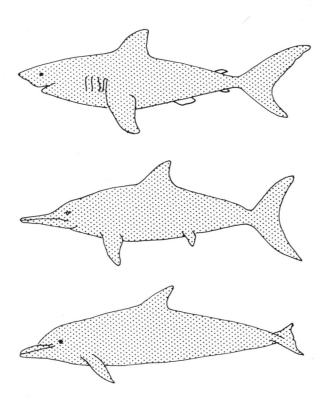

Above, top to bottom: The similar outlines of a shark, an icthyosaur (an extinct fish-like reptile), and a dolphin. All three, subject to the special demands of the marine environment, show convergent evolution in their body shape.

movements of the tail, whales and dolphins move their tails, or flukes, up and down.

The hydrodynamic efficiency of both sharks and dolphins is partly due to modifications in their skin. A shark's skin is covered by tiny, backward-pointing teeth called dermal denticles. A smooth skin would be subject to 'drag', or friction, as small vortices or areas of turbulence formed in the water passing over the skin. Small projections on the skin reduce turbulence and therefore drag. Taking their cue from nature, aircraft and yacht designers have experimented with tiny 'riblets' on aircraft and boat hulls to reduce drag and achieve greater speed and fuel efficiency. Dolphin skin, which feels like smooth wet velvet, is etched with microscopic ridges running transversely around the body – they're like the tiny ridges of a fingerprint. These may serve the same hydrodynamic purpose as shark denticles and aircraft riblets. Also, skin cells are continuously sloughed off as dolphins move through the water, another contribution to drag reduction.

Naval architects have been trying to come up with a similar covering for submarine hulls.

Another area of convergence relates to size and food gathering. The largest sharks and the largest whales are essentially filter-feeders. The giant whales take huge gulps of water and strain it through modified 'gum' projections known as baleen plates; these trap all the tiny organisms in the water. The largest shark, the whale shark, which grows up to 55 feet (16.8 meters) long and weighs over 20 tons, is a filter-feeder too. Water and food enter the broad, rectangular-shaped mouth, then, as the water is expelled through the gills, the gill rakers retain the food, which is then swallowed. Other giant sharks, such as the basking shark, the second largest fish in the sea after the whale shark, and the newly discovered megamouth are also filter-feeders. The basking shark skims the surface layers of the sea for plankton, while the megamouth swims in deeper water, feeding on a soup of deepsea crustaceans.

Smaller species of sharks and dolphins are built for

Above: The toothy profile of a sand tiger shark. Located in small pits in the snout are the electrical sensors on which the shark relies during the final moments of attack.

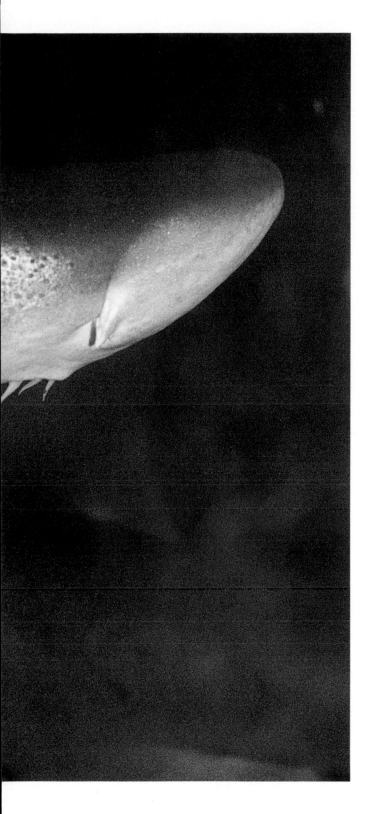

maneuverability and speed. For example, the bizarre projections on the head of a hammerhead shark enable it to turn in its own length. Since smaller species cannot simply scoop their food from the sea, they must chase and catch it, and so their senses are very highly developed.

In whales and dolphins, sound is the supreme sense. Dolphins hunt by sending out beams of very high-frequency sound and listening for the echoes that bounce back. As well as pinpointing the position of their prey they can also 'interrogate' it, establishing what species it is and whether it is alive or dead, relaxed or wary. It has also been suggested that dolphins, orcas, and sperm whales 'zap' and disable their prey with very high-intensity beams of sound.

Sharks rely on many senses, all of them highly tuned. A shark can smell blood or body fluids from a distance of a quarter of a mile (0.5 km) and unerringly follow an olfactory 'corridor' upcurrent towards a victim, comparing tiny differences in the current flow on either side of its body with sensory information picked up by its lateral line system. It can also hear and accurately locate low-frequency vibrations in the water, the kind made by struggling or wounded whales or dolphins. At 25 yards (23 meters), and almost in the dark, it can see the movement of prey, and in color. A shark's eyes are ten times more sensitive in dim light than human eyes, and can discriminate between blue, blue-green, and yellow. But if heading rapidly to the surface, perhaps to attack a seal or other surface-swimming creature from below, the retina quickly adapts so that it functions in bright light.

Above: The horny egg case of a dogfish, one of the smallest members of the shark family. A newly hatched dogfish is about 2 1/2 inches (10 cm) long. The tendrils at the corners of the case wind themselves around seaweed and underwater obstacles, anchoring the developing embryo and preventing mechanical damage.

Birth and parenthood

In whales and dolphins the developing embryo is retained inside the mother's body until is sufficiently developed to survive outside it. Babies and youngsters are then looked after by their mother, and also by aunties and other relatives. Extended families – the members of a 'pod' of orcas, for example, all belong to the same family – ensure that every individual is well protected, from the moment it is born to the moment it dies.

Sharks do not carry parental or family care quite as far as this, but they have a remarkable number of ways of bringing offspring into the world. The 368 species of sharks, which are classified as cartilaginous fishes, are often thought of as being more primitive than bony fishes, of which there are about 20,000 species. Some bony fishes, after all, show amazing devotion to their progeny – nest-guarding in cichlids, male 'pregnancy' in seahorses, mouth-breeding in the arawana.... But, in reality, the eggs of all bony fishes are fertilized externally and bony fish mothers produce hundreds, if not thousands, of eggs as a way of ensuring that least a few of them mature despite heavy predation. Many bony fishes show little parental care, leaving their eggs and young to fend for themselves.

Sharks on the other hand, like whales and dolphins, leave very little to chance. All sharks fertilize their eggs internally, produce a small number of offspring at a time, and give their pups a reasonable start in life.

Dogfish, which are small sharks, deposit up to 25 eggs at a time. These have a tough, rectangular, semi-transparent case, the familiar 'mermaid's purse', with tendrils at each corner which twine themselves around seaweed and other obstacles. The embryo inside is well protected until it is ready to hatch. Port Jackson sharks are also born from eggs. The mother lays 10 – 16 pencil-length eggs in shallow water, taking care to wedge them into crevices in the rocks; the eggs have two spiral flanges around them to prevent them being dislodged.

Many shark mothers play even safer and retain the developing embryos inside their body until they are sufficiently well developed to have a better-than-evens chance of survival in the outside world. In the majority of species, the embryos feed solely on self-contained yolk supplies, but some obtain most or all of their food directly from the mother.

The five fertilized eggs of the piked or spiny dogfish start their development enclosed in an amber-colored 'candle', or membrane, inside the mother. After six months the 'candle' ruptures or dissolves (no one is sure which) and the embryos continue to grow in the uterus for another 14 months, each feeding from its own yolk sac. At the end of the 22-month gestation period (the longest known for any shark and about the same as that of an African elephant), the pups emerge head first from the mother's cloacal opening. At this stage they are about 1 foot (25 cm) long. Each pup has its dorsal fin spines tipped with a blunt protective knob which falls off shortly after birth, presumably to make the birth less painful for the mother.

Hammerheads take things a stage further. For the first four months, the embryos feed on yolk, then their yolk sacs develop branches and attach themselves to the wall of the uterus like mini-placentas. Nutrients and oxygen from the mother's blood diffuse into the placentas, each attached to its embryo by an umbilical channel containing an artery, a vein, and a yolk canal. The young are born with an umbilical scar, but this disappears after a few weeks.

The most bizarre form of live birth occurs in ragged-toothed sharks, the group to which gray nurse and sand tiger sharks belong. In these species the uterus is divided, and a batch of fertilized eggs develops in both parts of the uterus. Then a strange thing happens. The most mature embryo in each uterus, having exhausted its yolk supply, eats its womb mates! The mother continues to ovulate and the two surviving embryos feed on a continuous supply of small unfertilized eggs, developing large, distended stomachs from eating so much yolk. When the two fully-formed intrauterine cannibals emerge, they must fend for themselves.

Some sharks protect their emerging offspring and ensure a ready supply of food for them by 'pupping' in traditional nursery areas where the water is warm, shallow, and teaming with small fish or invertebrates. Pregnant lemon sharks, for example, head for the shallow, horseshoe-shaped Bimini Lagoon in the Bahamas. Here their 2-foot (60-cm) long newborn pups can take refuge in the mangroves. Female bull sharks on the Florida coast enter the shallow lagoons of the Indian River, drop their pups, and quickly head back out to sea. The youngsters are left behind to feed on catfish and stingrays. The mothers do not feed

Above: Lemon sharks live in temperate coastal waters in the Atlantic and Eastern Pacific. They are rarely found at any depth, their small eyes being ill-adapted to dim light.

while they are at the pupping grounds, presumably to prevent cannibalism. During the pupping season male and female North American sandbar sharks form separate groups, probably for the same reason. The females stay inshore and in estuaries, and the males move to deeper water. Sex segregation is taken to extremes by North Atlantic blue sharks; the males remain on the East Coast of the United States, while the females migrate with the clockwise-flowing North Atlantic Gyre to pup off the coast of Portugal.

In most shark species parental care stops when the pups are born, but scalloped hammerheads seem to take their parental duties more seriously. Underwater photographer Jeremy Stafford-Deitsch was diving near the Sanageb coral atoll, northeast of Port Sudan in the

Red Sea, when he saw a shoal of scalloped hammerhead sharks swimming in an unusual formation at a depth of about 200 feet (60 meters). At the center of the formation was a tightly packed group of juveniles about 6 feet (1.8 meters) long, and forming a protective barrier around them were the larger adults.

Dolphins and whales sustain their newly-born youngsters with milk, as all mammals do. In fact, we humans have the dubious distinction of being the only mammal to drink milk – and the milk of other species at that – throughout our lives. But the synthesis of a liquid food intended to feed a newly-born or immature animal is not, it seems, unique to mammals. Tiger shark embryos are retained inside the body of the female – as many as 80 pups (but more normally 40) may be developing at any one time. To supplement the nutrients derived from their individual yolk sacs, the pups also feed on a creamy 'milk' secreted from the walls of the uterus.

Dispelling illusions

When sharks grow up, they bear the brunt of human persecution. They are the 'villains' of the natural world, not least because they make the mistake of eating people, or at least some of them do. Dolphins and whales are the gentle ones, the intelligent ones, the ones with whom – who knows? – we might one day hold meaningful conversations. But are whales and dolphins so angelic?

Humpback whale courtship groups are far from gentle. Bull humpbacks fight savagely for the right to mate with a female, butting each other, slapping flippers, and blowing bubbles – the whale equivalent of a 'raspberry' or 'Bronx cheer'. Right whales have great calcified callosities on their heads, probably for fighting. Killer whales hurl themselves onto the beaches of Patagonia to grab fur seals. Back in the water, they flip them high into the air, playing with them as casually as a cat plays with a mouse. In a Florida ocean circus, an animal trainer slipped into a killer whale pool and was torn to pieces in front of an arena full of horrified and unbelieving spectators.

In experiments with semi-captive common dolphins, an even more unappealing side of dolphin life came to light. Common dolphins from Sri Lanka and the Atlantic coast of Africa have different color patterns

and a slightly different body shape than those that live in Californian waters. African dolphins have a shorter snout and a mottled belly, and Sri Lankan dolphins have dark skin and wide lips. In the experiment, individuals from Asia and Africa were introduced to a group of Californian common dolphins and they were rejected. The Californian males ganged up on the 'foreign' dolphins, charging and butting them. When Californian individuals were sent to Africa and Sri Lanka, they were met with the same hostile treatment. In fact, one of the Californian dolphins was drowned by an African group, each member of the group taking it in turns to sit on the unfortunate visitor. In another test, dyes were used to change the color of a group of Californian dolphins and they were rejected by other members of their own school. The experimenters concluded that dolphins are color prejudiced!

What conclusions can we draw from such behavior? It is hard to say. When it comes to human or animal behavior, we tend to jump to amazing conclusions based on scanty knowledge. Perhaps we should conclude that our own prejudices – the image of the gentle whale, the friendly dolphin, and the vicious shark – may be misplaced.

Chapter 1

Whale fact file

The great whales, or rorquals, are the giants of our planet. The blue whale, for example, is probably the largest creature that has ever lived on earth, larger than the largest elephant, and larger than the largest dinosaur. The biggest specimen ever caught was a female that measured 109 feet (33.2 meters) from the tip of the snout to the notch between the tail flukes, and she weighed 200 tons. That was in 1926, off the South Shetland Islands in the South Atlantic. The heaviest elephant on record weighed a mere 11 tons.

Whales are powerful swimmers. With an up-and-down undulation of their great flukes, even the largest whales can work up sufficient impetus to leap clear of the water. Some have been been known to tow large boats. Blue and fin whales can cruise at about 5 miles per hour (9 km/h) for many miles, swim at 14 miles per hour (26 km/h) when in a hurry, and zip along at 20 miles per hour (37 km/h) when fleeing from danger. The more slender sei whale can attain a speed of 35 miles per hour (65 km/h) in short bursts.

Blubber reserves

One of the whale's most important attributes, apart from its body size, is the layer of fatty tissue, or blubber, that lies beneath the skin. Blubber has two functions: it keeps the whale warm and it stores energy in the form of fat. Many whales spend a great deal of time in polar seas and the insulating layer of blubber, which may be many inches thick, diminishes the amount of heat they lose to the surrounding water. During courtship, mating, and calving in tropical waters, and also during migration, many species do not feed. Indeed, some species fast for up to six months of

The seas around Antarctica contain vast supplies of krill, the tiny organisms on which the great baleen whales feed.

the year – their stores of blubber keep them going. When they arrive back in the polar oceans to feed, they have a significantly thinner layer of blubber. Whales that live all year round in good feeding areas, such as the fin whales that station themselves off eastern Canada, do not put on thick layers of blubber. Clearly they do not need vast reserves of fat since they are always able to feed. The blubber they have is for insulation only.

Whales are born without blubber, so have to put it on very quickly before they can swim to cold-water feeding grounds with their mothers. Whale milk is so rich that several inches of blubber are acquired in just a few weeks. During the first six months of its life, a blue whale calf gains weight at the rate of 8 1/2 lbs (3.85 kg) an hour! It receives 130 gallons (590 liters) of milk a day in about 40 feeds, more than an average human household consumes in a whole year.

A start in life

The early life of the right whale makes a particularly interesting study. Each year, in the southern winter, southern right whales calve in the shallow, sheltered bays of the Peninsula Valdès in Argentina. A single calf is born, about 18 feet (5.5 meters) long, and it stays in close contact with its mother for up to 14 months. No one has ever seen a right whale birth, but the calf is probably born tail first. The mother then helps it to the surface to take its first breath. Her nipples are on her belly, so the baby must learn to dive underneath her in order to suckle.

The growing calf is quite boisterous. It practices butting, diving, breaching, and rolling, pausing sometimes to rest on its mother's back. The mother never responds with the whale equivalent of a slap, not even when the calf covers her blowhole with its tail flukes. She simply endures her calf's high jinks and rolls over to embrace it with her flippers. However, learning to slap with the flippers is an important part of the calf's education – flipper-slapping is a way of communicating with other right whales and also of frightening away killer whales. Mother and calf form a self-contained unit, seldom mixing with other mothers and their calves, although many mother/calf pairs may be present in the same bay in what might be termed a 'loose' herd.

In November, the mother encourages her calf to firm up its muscles by swimming rapidly up and down the bay. This prepares it for the long journey to the feeding grounds in the Southern Ocean. The calf stays with the mother for the rest of its first year, returning to Peninsula Valdès the following winter. By this time it is fully weaned.

A yearling calf is semi-independent of its mother – if it strays, mom does not swim after it. Eventually she heads out to sea, leaving the calf in the company of other youngsters. She then spends the next year feeding in order to replenish the reserves she has lost while rearing her calf. The following year, she will be ready to breed again. Female right whales give birth to a single calf approximately every three years.

Breathing and diving

Whales are mammals and must therefore return to the surface at regular intervals to breathe. As, say, a large fin whale surfaces, the snout appears, then the blowhole, the rest of the back, and finally the tail. The whole body arches and then an upstroke of the tail pushes the whale back below the surface. In the couple of seconds that the blowhole is exposed, the whale expels the stale air from its lungs and draws in 500 gallons (2,270 litres) of fresh air. The expelled air has a typically oily smell.

In humans, only about 15 percent of the air in the lungs is exchanged in one breathing movement; in whales, the figure is nearer 90 percent. Whales have perfected the art of taking a quick, deep breath, and then holding it for a long time. Experienced pearl divers can hold their breath for about 2 1/2 minutes, hippos for 15 minutes, and beavers for 20. The great whales can stay submerged for 40 minutes, sperm whales for 90 minutes, and the beaked whales for up to two hours!

Whales are able to hold their breath for long periods because their muscles contain a dark red oxygen-storing pigment called myoglobin. Myoglobin enables

Right: Right whales courting in the shallow waters off Peninsula Valdès, Argentina. The male is on the left, the female being considerably larger. When mating takes place, the couple lie belly to belly with the male underneath. Mating pairs do not seem to form long-term bonds.

them to take their long, deep dives without running out of oxygen. Oxygen-rich blood can also be diverted to vital tissues such as the brain and swimming muscles. During deep dives, the heart slows down to two-thirds of its normal force and rate of contraction to reduce the amount of oxygen needed.

'Thar she blows!'

The blow, or spout, of a whale is an essential part of its breathing cycle, but to whale hunters a blow means a whale, and a whale means profit.

Each species of whale has its own distinctive spout. The spout of a right whale, for example, is V-shaped. Spouts are not always visible, but on windy days, when the water is rough, there is more water around the blowhole to turn to spray as the whale exhales. When traveling at speed, right whales breathe out underwater; this minimizes the time they spend at the surface refilling their lungs.

The rorquals have a single plume, but only skilled observers can recognize the spout of each species. On the old whaling ships, when a spout was sighted, whether it was the angled left-sided plume of a sperm whale or the high geyser of a blue whale, up would go the triumphant cry: 'Thar she blows!'

Whale talk

Most species of whale are vocal, but what do such vocalizations mean? Many whale experts believe that they convey information to other whales, information about individual, sexual, and species identity, and about location.

Blue whales produce very loud, deep moans that have been described as 'the most powerful sustained utterances known from whales or any other living source'. The notes drop gradually in pitch in a series of moans, and their sequence is very complex. Blue whales are also thought to produce high-frequency sounds.

The smaller minke whale produces bursts of low-frequency sounds known as 'thump trains'. Gray whales emit a series of clicks, rasps, and gong-like sounds. According to one expert, gray whale mothers and calves spend a lot of time 'talking to each other'. Right whales make a deep bellowing sound, sometimes interspersed with high-frequency chirps.

Humpback whales have been heard 'singing' for hours on end at their tropical breeding grounds. Their songs have tremendous carrying power, being audible on hydrophones 100 miles (160 km) away. Only the males sing, presumably to attract a mate or warn other males to keep away. Intensive study has revealed that at any given time during the mating season all the male

humpbacks in a specific population sing exactly the same song, but the song changes throughout the season. A dominant animal in the population probably rings the changes and all the others follow suit. As the season progresses, the pitch of the song deepens until, to the human ear, the sounds are so low that they are felt rather than heard. Singing sessions usually last for 5 – 30 minutes, with some individuals singing for many hours without interruption. When a singer surfaces to breathe, he does not end his recital but chooses a natural pause in the song to snatch a breath.

A singing whale is almost always alone, well away from other singers. If he is approached by a female, he stops singing and swims along with her, or he may spot a cow with her calf and head toward her. If she is receptive, and not already mated, he stops singing and becomes her escort. Cow, calf, and escort will then swim slowly together. At intervals the cow and her escort dive into the depths, leaving the calf at the surface. It is believed that this is when they mate.

After a while, male and female return to the surface and the trio continues along at a fairly leisurely pace.

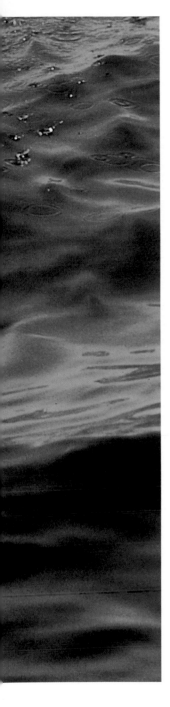

Above: The spout of a southern right whale. Note the callosities on the head, the coaming in front of the nostrils, and the 'post blowhole island' behind them.

Left: In the fin whale, there is a long ridge between the blowhole and the snout. Fin whales are known to make loud, low-frequency sounds of almost pure tone that can be heard hundreds of miles away under the sea. Fins are usually spotted swimming in pairs, but each pair may be part of a gigantic herd widely dispersed across the ocean. The sounds they make may be a way of keeping in contact with each other. Such 'conversations' are easily interrupted by the throbbing of supertanker engines.

Often another singer will see them, stop singing, and approach. The second male will then fight with the first for the privilege of escorting the female. The two suitors blow bubbles at each other, butt their heads together, and slap each other with their long flippers. The swimming speed of the group gradually increases and other singers, attracted by the commotion, approach the group and join in the fray. Eventually, they become bored and swim away to take up new singing positions.

Mating in whales must be a great but delicate affair.

Male southern right whales are very gentle. Several may vie for a female's attention, but there is little hostility between them. The female rebuffs her suitors by lying belly-up in the water, but the amorous males wait patiently until she runs out of air and is forced to turn over. At this point they swim in and jostle for the best position to mate.

Right: A right whale and her calf swim in sheltered waters off the Peninsula Valdès in Argentina. Many whales choose sheltered bays and shallow lagoons in which to mate and give birth.

Below: A humpback whale pushes its head out of the water to have a good look around. This is known as 'spy-hopping'.

Above: A humpback whale breaching. About 45 tons of whale lift almost clear of the water and crash down in an explosion of spray. Some researchers believe that breaching is a form of communication, particularly in rough, wind-blown seas when conventional vocal sounds would be inaudible.

Below: A humpback whale swims belly-up off the coast of Massachusetts. The belly and the underside of the flippers and flukes are white. The folds on the throat allow enormous expansion of the mouth cavity when the whale is feeding.

Above: *An underwater view of a humpback whale. Being slow swimmers, humpbacks were the staple of the early Antarctic whaling industry. Despite complete protection since 1964, today's stocks are probably 90 percent below their pre-exploitation level.*

Below: Euphausia superba, *the Antarctic krill, is by far the most important of the tiny shrimp-like crustáceans on which baleen whales and many other marine creatures feed. Krill themselves feed on tiny microorganisms, or plankton, and can grow to a length of 6 ¹/₂ inches (16 cm) in the short Antarctic summer. Mile-wide swarms containing several millions tons of krill float just below the surface. Humpbacks and other species of baleen whale steadily graze their way through this living soup.*

Above and below: Two views of the unmistakable knobbly head of a humpback whale. The shallow upper jaw bears the baleen bristles. Separate populations of humpbacks live in all the oceans of the world, migrating from breeding grounds in tropical waters to summer feeding grounds at high latitudes north and south. Northern Pacific humpbacks spend the summer feeding around the Aleutian Islands and off the coast of Alaska, taking a wide variety of foods, including fish and tiny crustaceans. In the Southern Ocean around Antarctica, supplies of krill are so abundant that fish are only an occasional food.

This page: Beluga whales in the shallow waters of Barrow Strait, Canadian Arctic. Belugas, also known as white whales, are among the most vocal of whales - the old whalers called them 'sea canaries'. They have a highly complex repertoire of squeals, resonant chirps, clucks, trills, and other sounds suggesting a group of children shouting in the distance! Young belugas are dark, but whiten as they mature. For about six weeks every summer, belugas splash around in shallow water to clean themselves, shedding the yellow coating of diatoms that accumulates throughout the rest of the year. Belugas are toothed whales, and feed on polar cod, halibut, and molluscs. No mass strandings have ever been reported. Stranded individuals can survive for at least 12 hours out of water, unless killed by hunting Inuit or polar bears.

Above: A narwhal mother and calf. Calves are born in July as the females reach their far-northern summering grounds. Gestation takes about 15 months.

Left: Narwhals have no dorsal fin, although the back is ridged toward the tail. In adult males, the trailing edge of the flukes becomes convex.

Below: An aerial view of a pod of male narwhals photographed off the coast of East Greenland. Narwhals are toothed whales, similar in size to belugas (up to about 16 feet/5meters), and only the males have tusks, occasionally used for fighting. The tusk is the massive, spiral outgrowth of the left upper front tooth; very occasionally, both front teeth grow, producing a pair of tusks! The rest of the teeth are non-functional. At one time, narwhal tusks were thought to be the horns of the mythical 'unicorn' and were prized for their magical powers. Narwhals are seen farther north than any other whale, moving out to sea in winter and into coastal waters in summer.

Chapter 2

A whale called orca

The most notorious whale of all, the killer whale, has a reputation for ferocity that is only partly deserved. In the interests of objectivity, scientists now prefer to call it the orca, after its species name *Orcinus orca*, and that is the name we will use throughout the rest of this book.

Orcas are the largest and fastest of the dolphins – dolphins are merely smaller members of the order Cetacea to which the whales belong. Males orcas can grow to a length of 26 feet (8 meters) or more and females to about 23 feet (7 meters), and they are capable of speeds of 30 miles per hour (55 km/h). Orcas are black and white, with a gray saddle behind the dorsal fin. In the male the dorsal fin is upright, triangular, and up to 6 feet (1.8 meter) tall; in the female it is a little smaller and slightly backward-curving.

Orcas live in 'pods', or family groups, with up to 40 animals in each pod. Pods tend to stay together for life, although sometimes a very large pod splits into two.

Along the Pacific coast of Canada, near Vancouver, there are resident pods and transient pods. The residents live in the area all year round, while the transients merely pass through at certain times of year. Scientists have been able to group the resident pods into distinctive clans on the basis of their vocalizations – members of the same clan share the same repertoire of sounds, an indication of their common descent from an ancient pod that grew too big.

Hunting in packs

Orcas hunt cooperatively, the adults and older juveniles doing all the work while the youngsters hang around for the pickings. Off the coast of Vancouver, where orcas have been closely studied, Pacific salmon are a

The dorsal fin of an orca rises ominously above a steel-gray sea.

favorite food. When hunting, orcas fan out into a line, like a row of beaters, coordinating their movements with whistles, honks, and squawks. Then they swim toward the rocky shore, herding the salmon in front of them. To prevent the salmon escaping, they slap the water loudly with their flippers and flukes, and make great leaps out of the water, followed by thunderous belly-flops. When the fish are well and truly trapped, the orcas dart in and grab them, giving them a brief crunch before swallowing. When they have fed well, orcas have a habit of playing with their prey, just as a cat plays with a mouse.

Orcas are found all over the world, but are far more common in colder latitudes where food – in the form of squid, sharks and other fish, seabirds, penguins, seals, sealions, other dolphins, and large whales – is more abundant. Orcas are the only toothed whales that actively prey upon other mammals, but they rarely put human beings on the menu. On occasion, orcas have been known to poke their black and white heads out of the waves and seriously study the occupants of small boats, but they usually ignore people who fall overboard. In captivity, with very few exceptions, they are gentle and playful.

There are some interesting reports of encounters between orcas and humans. In 1911, H.L. Ponting, the photographer on Captain Scott's second Antarctic expedition, was standing on an ice-floe when it was rammed by a couple of orcas. This could have been a case of mistaken identity, for orcas often try to upset ice platforms occupied by seals or penguins in order to tip them into the water, or it could have been mere curiosity.

In 1956, off the coast of British Columbia, two lumberjacks were pushing logs into the water. One of them deliberately set a log to ram one of a group of orcas swimming nearby. The orcas disappeared. But when the lumberjacks were rowing back to camp, the orcas returned, capsized the boat, and the man who had provoked them was never seen again. His companion was unharmed and lived to tell the tale.

During a skindiving competition along the Californian coast in 1962, a group of orcas, searching for seals and sealions among the giant kelp beds, approached and checked out each diver in turn before swimming on their way. None of the divers was molested.

In 1976, off the coast of Brazil, a large Italian yacht was rammed by orcas. The crew had to swim from the sinking vessel to the lifeboat, but the orcas totally ignored them.

But it is a very different story with baleen whales. Where possible, baleen whales steer well clear of orcas. A pack of hungry orcas can tear a whale to pieces, but they are choosy about the bits they eat – just the skin, the blubber, the dorsal fin, the tongue, and the flesh of the lower jaw.

Along the coast of southern California packs of orcas lie in wait for the arrival of the gray whales each year, preying on calves and juveniles rather than adults. An adult minke whale that got into difficulties in shallow water was 'drowned' by an orca stopping its blowhole and then ripping it apart. On another occasion, this time off the southern coast of Alaska, orcas were seen molesting a pair of humpback whales. At first, the biologist watching the scene thought the humpbacks were chasing a group of orcas. Then he realized that the humpbacks were twisting and turning in the water and being attacked from behind by a second group of orcas, who were taking bites at their bellies. Eventually, more humpbacks arrived on the scene, joined the wounded pair, and swam along in tight formation with them. The orcas backed off, but nevertheless hung around for three hours or so, constantly swimming in and looking for weak spots. An old or infirm humpback would have been torn to pieces. Typically, the orcas were working as a tight-knit, coordinated unit.

Star performers

In captivity, orcas are gentle and even friendly. They seem to enjoy being stroked, admired, and allowed to display their virtuosity. They are popular with both trainers and visitors because they learn fast and perform quite amazing tricks.

Orcas are the largest of the 'performing' dolphins and also the most expensive. Many millions of dollars change hands when orcas are procured from the wild. Most are caught near Iceland. An animal that would have cost about $8,000 in the late 1960s can now fetch more than $500,000, but the trade is kept very secret. Young orcas are the most sought after as they are easier to train and cheaper to feed. A 10-year-old orca that lived in Windsor Safari Park, England, used to eat

175 pounds (84 kg) of fish a day!

For the few orcas that make it to dolphinaria there are many that die. Stressed or injured animals – those held in makeshift conditions for long periods of time, for example, or those who suffer from frostbite – are surreptitiously released back into the wild, usually at night. They probably die soon after.

Below: Orcas have a large gape, with a single row of backward-pointing teeth in the upper and lower jaw. These interlock as the mouth closes. The force of the bite can tear a seal in two. One orca was found with the remains of 13 dolphins and 14 seals in its stomach, although not all of these would have been devoured at the same meal.

Above: An orca menacing a group of South American sealions. During the sealion breeding season, orcas regularly fling themselves onto steeply-shelving beaches in pursuit of seals and sealions, but they very rarely become stranded.

Left: Several orcas hunting in the surf off Peninsula Valdès in Argentina. Orcas are the only whales that regularly take warm-blooded prey as well as fish and squid.

Below: Three orcas 'gang up' on a solitary seal on an Antarctic ice floe. Orcas are quite capable of upsetting such ice platforms and tipping their occupants into the sea. Only Ross seals occasionally swim fast enough to escape.

Below: An orca breaching in Puget Sound, off the coast of Washington. Young orcas can leap 20 feet (6 meters) into the air. Orcas can choose whether to re-enter the water head first, causing little disturbance, or land with an enormous splash. This is what they do when they are driving fish inshore. A fish-drive is a cooperative effort, with all the adult members of the pod executing a military-style 'pincer' movement.

Left and inset: A pod of orcas patrols the still waters of Glacier Bay, Alaska, on the lookout for humpback whales. The tall, vertical dorsal fin of the male is easily distinguished from that of his female companions.

Left and above: Orcas at Miami go through their routines for the benefit of visitors. In the U.S. Navy 'Deep Ops' program, two orcas, Ishmael and Ahab, were trained to attach recovery devices to objects on the seabed. Unfortunately, Ishmael made off in a huff, never to be seen again, and Ahab refused to work!

Right: A pilot whale performing at Redwood City, California. The U.S. Navy 'Deep Ops' program also trained a pilot whale named Morgan for seabed recovery duties. Morgan, unlike Ishmael and Ahab, did not fail his trainers. He dived to a depth of 2,000 feet (610 meters) and satisfactorily completed all his tasks.

Far right: Captive orcas have dispelled many cherished myths about 'killer whales'. They are gentle animals and quick to learn tricks. 'You have the distinct feeling, though', said one trainer, 'that the whale is in charge and not the trainer.'

Left and above: Today, most people are likely to have their first sight of orcas in a zoo or aquarium. But our ancestors seem to have been more familiar with the species. In Scotland, orca bones have been uncovered in ancient garbage dumps, or 'middens'. In southern France, prehistoric man scratched pictures of orcas onto cave walls. In AD 60, the Roman historian Pliny the Elder recorded the fact that an orca had become trapped in shallow water off the port of Ostia, near Rome.

Right: The high dorsal fin of the male orca certainly looks like some kind of weapon. Schwertwal, meaning 'sword whale', is the German name for the species. The Japanese name, sakatama, means 'halberd'.

Chapter 3

Long-distance voyages

Because observation in the open ocean is extremely difficult, social groupings among whales are tricky to study. Groups varying in number from two to twelve individuals have been seen, but on average whales appear to move about in pairs or threes. This may be for feeding reasons. The krill and bait fish on which the largest whales feed occur in vast quantities at the ocean surface, but in a very patchy fashion. If many whales converged on a single patch, the pickings would be scanty; there would be plenty for two or three whales, but too much for one. Also, a large group making lots of noise would attract orcas and sharks; equally, a solitary whale would be no match for an orca pack. Herds of migrating whales maximize their chances of survival by traveling in widely dispersed small groups.

The gray whales are coming!

More than a million Canadians and Americans drive to vantage points along the Pacific coast in spring and fall each year to see the north and south migrations of the gray whale. From rocky promontories and from special whale-watch boats, they witness part of the longest mammal migration in the world. Gray whales make an annual round trip of 12,500 miles (20,000 km) from the Alaskan Arctic to Baja California in Mexico, hugging the coast for most of the way. They swim slowly, blowing frequently and 'spy-hopping', or poking their enormous barnacled heads out of the water to check their bearings.

On the journey south, they seem to adopt a policy of 'women and children first'. The pregnant females swim out ahead, racing for the shallow lagoons where they will drop their calves. They are followed by recently mated females, and immature females and calves, and the adult males bring up the rear.

The northward journey is equally orderly. This time, the newly mated females swim in front. They will

Humpback whales on the first stage of their journey south to Baja California.

47

be the first to arrive at the northern feeding grounds, maximizing feeding opportunities for themselves and their growing calves. Following them are the adult males, non-breeding females, and immature males. Behind them come the mothers and calves.

Many packs of orcas frequent the migration route, so the whales swim close inshore, seeking the protection of the giant kelp beds that fringe the Pacific coast.

Seafood cocktails

Between June and October, the gray whales and humpback whales of the Eastern Pacific live and feed off the coast of Alaska. In spring, as the pack ice retreats and the organisms that have settled on the seabed are stirred into growth, there is a superabundance of food. There are plankton 'blooms' and the sea becomes a rich soup of tiny crustaceans and fish fry. Now is the time for the whales to feed up. What they eat now will have to sustain them for most of the year.

Gray whales feed in shallow water. They dive to the bottom, turn on their right side, and plow their snout through the sediment on the sea floor, sucking in crustaceans, worms, molluscs, and mud. As they return to the surface, they force water through their baleen plates, which sieves out the food. Glaucous gulls, Arctic terns, and horned puffins wait for the morsels that fall from the whales' mouths. Although preoccupied with mating and calving during their time in the shallow bays of Baja California, gray whales do occasionally scour the sea bottom there for tasty crabs and shrimps.

Humpback whales have a unique feeding method. It is called 'bubble-netting'. The whale dives below a shoal of small bait fish and herring and casts a 'net' of bubbles. As the bubbles rise, they form a column that surrounds the fish and forces them to the surface. It is thought that the whale can adjust the size of the bubbles, the 'mesh' of the 'net', to hold victims of varying sizes. The whale then swims up, open-mouthed, through the center of the column, engulfing the fish plus hundreds of gallons of water. Pleats in the lower jaw bulge to accommodate the water, then the lower jaw is raised and the water is forced out through the baleen plates. The whales then licks the fish off the inside of the baleen plates with its very muscular tongue and swallows.

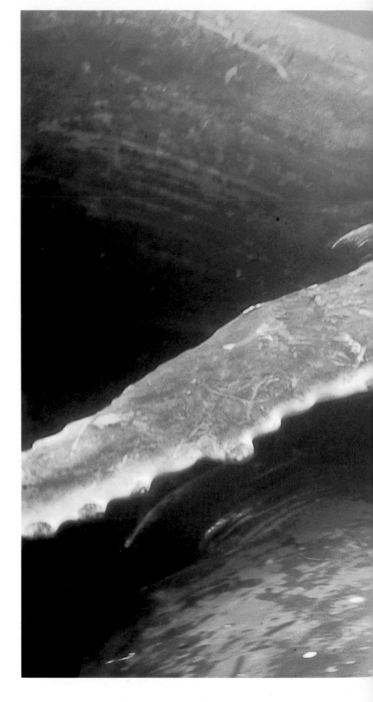

Humpbacks also indulge in 'flick-feeding'. This involves swimming just below the surface and suddenly flexing the tail, checking forward movement and generating a wave through which the whale swims with its mouth wide open. The wave seems to concentrate small food items, although precisely how this happens is far from clear. Humpbacks also use their very long flippers to direct krill into their mouths. They also 'lunge' at small shoals of fish, coming up from below, turning at the last moment, and sweeping one huge flipper out of the water and down again with

Left: A humpback calf hitches a ride on its mother's back, resting its chin on her blowhole. Note how shallow the upper jaw is compared with the lower. Adult humpbacks reach about 50 feet (15.2 meters) in length. Researchers identify individuals by the white markings under the flukes and on the leading edge of the flippers.

a great splash. Groups of six or seven humpbacks have been seen lunge-fishing in line abreast, communicating with each other by grunting sounds.

Generally speaking, baleen whales fall into two main groups as far as feeding is concerned: skimmers and gulpers. Bowheads and right whales tend to be skimmers, while blue whales are gulpers. A blue whale weighing 200 tons can 'gulp' down 8 tons of krill a day. But the same species of whale may feed differently in different parts of the ocean. Minke and fin whales in the North Atlantic and North Pacific have a slightly

different diet from their southern cousins. Pacific minkes eat inshore stocks of saffron cod, while Atlantic minkes not only eat fish but are also seen feeding with fin whales that are gulping and sieving krill. Fin whales in the Atlantic eat fish and krill, while their Pacific relatives feed on fish, krill, and squid.

But those who eat are also eaten! The great baleen whales are plagued by parasites and predators. The orca comes top of the predator list, followed by sharks. Until a few years ago, scientists were puzzled by the small, circular bites often seen in whale blubber, and

*Above and top right: A tourist and a film-maker enjoy a close
encounter with gray whales off the coast of Baja California.
However, gray whales can be dangerous. Early whalers called
them 'devil fish' from their habit of ramming and sinking small
boats. Females and juveniles, though, are known as 'friendlies'
and often come close to tourist boats, nuzzling up and allowing
inquisitive hands to touch their rubbery skin. At one time it
was feared that the number of sightseeing boats would interfere
with the whales' natural behavior, but now it is thought that
the whales actually enjoy such contacts.*

attributed them to lampreys. Then they realized that
the culprit was the small cookie-cutter shark, which
sneaks up on the swimming whale, sinks its teeth into
the skin and blubber, then allows the forward
movement of the whale to twist its body free. As it
detaches itself from the whale, it takes a cookie-size
piece of flesh with it.

Below: A humpback waves a flipper to a boatload of whale-watchers off the coast of Masschusetts. Western Atlantic humpbacks spend the summer off Newfoundland, Greenland, and Iceland, moving south to the Caribbean to breed.

Far left: Pilot whales being caught in the Faroe Islands. The grind, drive-fishing for pilot whales, is a tradition that goes back to Viking times. The whales are encircled by small boats and driven toward the shore, where they are hauled up and killed.

Left: Migrating humpbacks entangled in drift nets off Newfoundland. The nets are usually destroyed and the whales drown.

Below: Holidaymakers in Tasmania attempting to return a school of stranded pilot whales to the sea. Confused and exhausted, rescued animals often beach themselves again and again before finally swimming off.

Far left: The flukes of humpbacks often show the distinctive marks of orca teeth. The trailing edge of the flukes of this individual have been severely nibbled. Other parts of the body are blotched and scarred with patches of barnacles, or bear the scars made by cookie-cutter sharks.

Left: This is the head and mouth of a cookie-cutter shark. Small but ferocious, cookie-cutter sharks specialize in biting neat, circular plugs of flesh out of deep-diving whales and large fish. Cookie-cutters are adapted to deep water — the eyes see well in near darkness, and the head and belly are strongly luminescent. One species of cookie-cutter has the largest teeth relative to its size of any species of shark.

Below: Some humpbacks preface bubble-net and lunge-feeding by leaping out of the water and lob-tailing, or smacking the surface of the water with their tail flukes.

Above: When they are actively feeding, humpback whales are often surrounded by an excited gaggle of seabirds. Occasonally a bird is accidentally swallowed! Humpbacks certainly communicate with each other when they are at their feedings grounds, but they rarely 'sing'.

Above: These two humpbacks have completed their 'bubble-net' maneuver – they have closed their mouths and are about to force the water out through their baleen bristles, leaving thousands of krill and small fish behind.

Baleen is made of a flexible substance called keratin, which growns down from the 'gums' of the upper jaw. It is not a replacement for teeth, which are present, though vestigial. The first whales to be equipped with baleen evolved about 35 million years ago.

Left: A large humpback, with mouth wide open and throat vastly distended, surfaces in the center of a 'bubble-net'. Water streams from the baleen bristles fringing the upper jaw. The amount of krill and small fish concentrated in the rising net of bubbles is far greater than in the surrounding water.

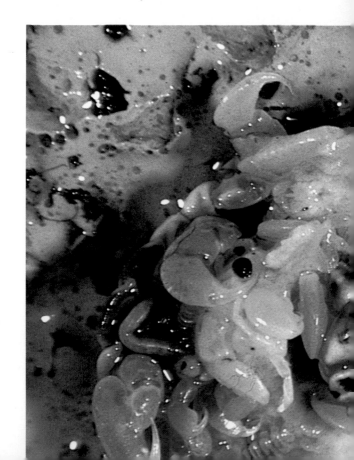

*Above: Gray whales hold the record for skin parasites.
This individual even has a barnacle growing on its blowhole.
Different species of barnacle favour different parts of the
whale's body, with the stalked ones tending to live on top of
the conical ones. When their host enters fresh or brackish
water, many of them drop off, unable to tolerate the low
salinity. It is thought that 'breaching' may be a way of
dislodging such hitch-hikers.*

*Above right: A patch of barnacles provides an ideal micro-
climate for whale lice, the crab-like parasites that have a
particular liking for gray whales.*

*Right: A close-up of whale lice on a gray whale's skin.
A single whale may be host to more than 100,000
whale lice. They feed on flaking skin and on the pieces
of food that spill from the whale's mouth.*

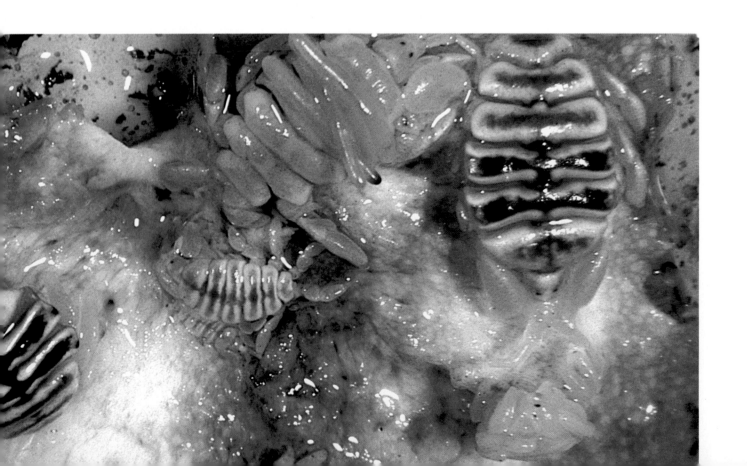

Chapter 4

Fighting to survive

From time immemorial, coastal peoples of the world have hunted whales. In Norway, there are 4,000-year-old rock drawings of whales and in Alaska archaeologists have found whale bones in 3,500-year-old garbage dumps.

Early whale hunters were few in number and inefficient, and they only caught inshore species. The Inuit of North America hunted bowhead and northern right whales, and the smaller belugas and narwhals, from single-seat kayaks of sealskin or from umiaks crewed by several men. Grays and humpbacks on their migrations up and down the Pacific coast of North America were hunted by the Dene and other Indian tribes. The Haida of what is now British Columbia went whale-hunting in 35-foot (10-meter) dugout canoes made of cedar. The harpoons they used were made of yew wood tipped with the sharp edge of an abalone shell.

In the Aleutian Islands, in the northern Pacific, whale-hunters tipped their harpoons with a poison extracted from the monkswood plant. Having speared their whale, they would wait until it died, decomposed, and floated to the surface. Further south, on the western side of the Pacific, the Japanese caught humpbacks in large nets; the *coup de grâce* was delivered by a swimmer with a long lance.

Even when sailing ships enabled whalers to exploit deepwater species, and the demand for whale oil was high, the impact of hunting on whale numbers was not too serious. It was not until the middle of the nineteenth century, when the steamship and the harpoon gun were invented, that hunting really began to threaten whale stocks.

The early whalers voyaged to the whaling grounds in sailing ships and transferred to rowing boats for the hunt. They would hurl hand-held harpoons into the whale, make the harpoon line fast to a post on the bow of the rowing boat, and then hang on for their lives as

The explosive horror of a whale hunt captured from high up in the crow's nest.

the whale towed them about the ocean. When the whale was exhausted they killed it, waited for their ship to catch up with them, and flensed the whale alongside the ship. They could only take small whales; the larger species, such as the blue and the fin, were left alone.

Modern whaling

The first harpoon guns were mounted on the bows of steamships, which had the speed to chase even the largest whales. These guns fired barbed darts that opened out once they were embedded in the whale. Often, as the frantic whale dived fast and deep, the dart would pull out, but the whale would die later from its wounds.

It was Svend Foyn, a Norwegian sea captain, who invented the modern harpoon gun and explosive harpoon. During the first test in 1894, the harpoon line caught his leg and pulled him overboard, but he survived. Two years later he perfected the invention that was to devastate the great whale populations of the world and drive them nearly to extinction.

When Foyn's harpoon was fired into a whale and the barbs began to open, a small glass phial of sulfuric acid was crushed and a cylinder of gunpowder was ignited. The resulting explosion, except when directly in the brain, did not kill the whale immediately. In great agony, the whale would dive deep, occasionally returning to the surface to breathe. When its spout turned red with blood, the whalers knew the end was near. The whale would die writhing in what was picturesquely known as a 'flurry'.

The dead whale was then brought alongside, lanced, and an air hose pushed inside it. It was then pumped up with air to prevent it sinking and also to make it easier to tow back to the shore base or factory ship. Or it might be left floating in the sea 'in flag', with the whaling's company's flag flying from poles stuck into its body, ready for the mother ship to come and collect it. As an extra safeguard, identity notches were cut in the flukes.

The deadly numbers game

Whaling ships today are diesel-powered and equipped with sonar and other devices to make hunting easier.

The five-year ban on commercial whaling introduced in 1987 by the International Whaling Commission, to which whaling and non-whaling nations belong, has never been 100 percent effective. Special permits are issued for 'scientific purposes' and unscrupulous nations, following the letter rather than the spirit of this provision, continue to take minke, fin, sei, and sperm whales. This is whaling disguised as science, for the flesh is sold on the open market. The traditional whaling nations – Iceland, Norway, and Japan – are now pressing for a resumption of commercial whaling, arguing that minke whale stocks, if not stocks of other whales as well, are sufficiently recovered to support limited takes in specified areas. Whale conservationists are doubtful of this and are very worried indeed.

It is thought that there are no more than 500 blue whales left in the southern hemisphere, and this after several decades of protection. Population estimates made in the 1960s are now thought to have been flawed; whalers took too many blue whales when the killing of these gentle giants was allowed. Whale scientists are now concerned that they might have got the numbers wrong with other species and argue that any resumption of commercial whaling could be disastrous. In 1990, aboriginal whalers were allowed to take 364 whales, including the very rare bowhead whale and the vulnerable humpback. Minke, fin, and sei whales will continue to be taken for 'scientific purposes'.

Sadly, large numbers of whales die each year as a result of human error and negligence. Lost or abandoned fishing nets – mile-long drift nets, for example continue to catch fish, seals, whales, dolphins, and seabirds indiscriminately. 'Ghost fishing', as it is called, accounts for many whale and dolphin deaths each year. Off the coast of Newfoundland, a maze of drift nets is cast into the sea each summer to catch spawning shoals of small fish. Unfortunately, the nets are in the path of migrating humpback whales, which feed on the spawning fish on their journey through. Many humpbacks become trapped in the nets and drown.

In the summer of 1984, eight Californian gray whales died from toxic chemicals. Someone had decanted wood preservative into the Serpentine River and the preservative found its way into the Strait of Georgia. The whales died of acute liver damage. In the mouth of the St. Lawrence, on Canada's eastern

Above: An Icelandic catcher boat with a fin whale in tow. A drop in the fin whale population has contributed to a massive increase in the krill population, a bounty taken advantage of by seals and seabirds.

seaboard, beluga whales are failing to reproduce. The reproductive tracts of the females have been so affected by pollutants washed down the St. Lawrence that they are unable to conceive or bear calves. This particular population will eventually disappear.

Ecological upsets

Whales have come near to extinction because every part of their body can be used to make some artefact or other. The consequence of intense hunting has been a far-reaching ecological imbalance in areas where whales were once common. In the Southern Ocean, for example, the killing of large numbers of fin and blue

whales has resulted in a massive increase in the krill population. More krill has therefore become available to other species. This has resulted in an increase in the population of crabeater seals, Antarctic fur seals, penguins, and seabirds. Also, those whales that do survive – blues, fins, and smaller whales such as seis and minkes – are giving birth at an earlier age and with greater frequency than before. Up until the 1930s, female fin whales matured and had their first calf at about ten years old. Now they mature at six years. Minkes have reduced their maturity from fourteen to six years. It is hoped, therefore, that the populations of these whales will bounce back up to their former numbers.

Below: An Azorean whaler about to harpoon a sperm whale in the Western Atlantic.

Right: The harpooned whale has towed the boat for many miles and is now exhausted. The harpooner prepares to despatch it with a lance. The whale will then be hauled back to shore to be 'flensed' or cut up.

Right: Modern whaling ships are equipped with large steel harpoons launched from powerful harpoon guns.

Below: The controversial 'cold grenade' harpoon does not explode inside the whale's body; instead the barbs open up, tearing painfully into the flesh. Large shore stations on South Georgia in the South Atlantic were once served by boats carrying such harpoons. Small shore stations were also used by whalers operating in the Azores, and from St. Vincent and St. Lucia in the West Indies.

Right: The 'plan' or flensing platform of an abandoned whaling station on South Georgia. Most whales are now caught, in the name of 'science', from catcher boats that serve a factory ship. Before the International Whaling commission ban, Norwegian catcher boats caught minke whales in the northeast Atlantic and North Sea.

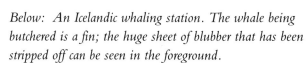

Below: An Icelandic whaling station. The whale being butchered is a fin; the huge sheet of blubber that has been stripped off can be seen in the foreground.

69

Below: These are the belly corrugations of a fin whale. The flenser slits the skin with a flensing knife to free the blubber, which contains the oil. Skin and blubber are then be stripped off by steam-winch.

There are now viable substitutes for most whale products. Sperm whale oil, for example, used as a high-grade lubricant, can be replaced by oil extracted from the jojoba shrub. The Apache Indians used jojoba oil in their lamps and as a balm for aching joints.

Right: A sperm whale tooth carved with a memento of a visit to the Fiji Islands in 1877. Pieces like this, known as 'scrimshaw', are much sought after by collectors.

Below right: Chunks of sperm whale blubber hanging up to dry in in Indonesia. Native hunters take small numbers of whales each year.

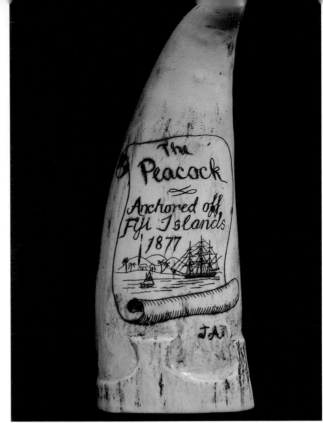

A gray whale breaching. Gray whales are recognized by their lack of a dorsal fin and by their blotched gunmetal-gray coloration. The older the individual, the more plentiful the scars and patches of barnacles.

Grays have many nicknames, besides 'Devil fish'. They are also known as 'mussel-diggers', from their habit of disturbing the bottom sediments and surfacing with mud and debris streaming from their mouths, and as 'hardheads', from their penchant for ramming boats. They were hunted to the edge of extinction in the late nineteenth century, but have been protected since 1947. Today the species has almost regained its former numbers.

Below: A posse of orcas lies in wait for gray whales moving north to their summer feeding grounds.

This page: The ribs of a southern right whale on a beach in the South Orkneys.

Inset: A collection of whale bones – ribs and vertebrae – near an abandoned whaling station in South Georgia. At one time the plates of baleen in the mouths of filter-feeding baleen whales was referred to as 'whalebone'. Whalebone was used to stiffening ladies' corsets, and to make umbrella ribs, riding crops, and clock springs. Bowhead whales have the longest baleen plates (up to 15 feet/4.5 meters long).

Left: Minke whales, the smallest of the rorquals, would bear the brunt of commercial whaling, if the IWC ban were to be lifted.

Below: The flukes of a blue whale flip briefly above the Southern Ocean. Blue whales can be distinguished from fin and sei whales by the way the tail comes out of the water before they dive. Very little is known about their numbers or their distribution, but the few that are left are proof that there are still giants in the sea.

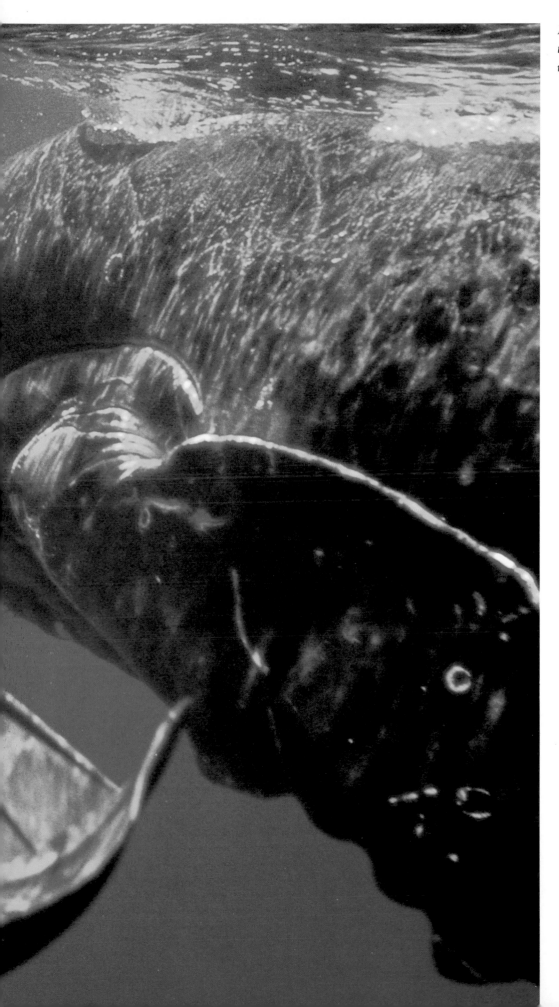

Left: A diver approaches the snout of a humpback whale.

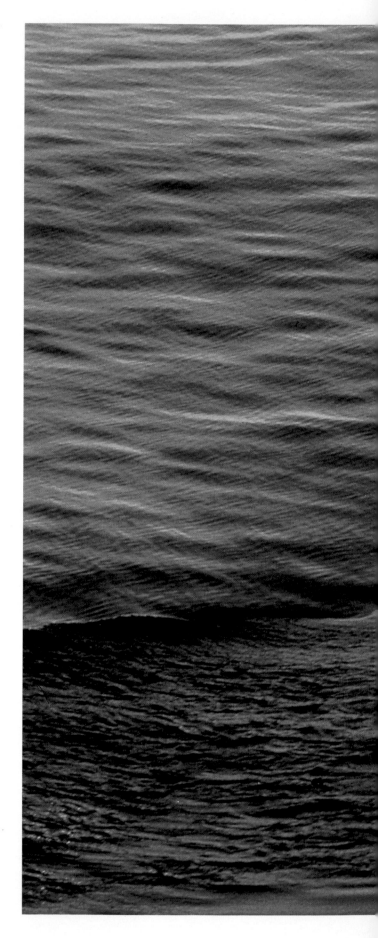

Chapter 5

Sonics and ultrasonics

'Whenever I go into the water, he joins me. He slaps his flippers on the surface as a hello and then dances around me, diving down, spiraling, brushing against my legs....The first time he nosed his way under me, lifted me onto his back and took me for a ride, I was scared, but only for a moment. He was so big! But he went slowly and was very gentle with me. Now those rides are my happiest moments. There's nothing like it. I hold onto his fin and we're off.' So wrote a 13-year-old girl who lived in New Zealand.

Dolphins are small whales, and they inhabit nearly all the seas of the world, and some of its rivers too. Highly intelligent, they have been working their way into human affections for thousands of years, at least since the time of the Ancient Greeks. In all the dolphin stories that exist, not one tells of a dolphin harming a human being. In fact the opposite is true. Dolphins have helped sailors in distress, fishermen in trouble, and swimmers who have lost their way. Some stories even imply that dolphins have ESP (extrasensory perception) and can telepathically understand human thoughts and moods. Perhaps this notion is romantic, but there is definitely an affinity between human beings and dolphins, and the more we come to know about our water cousins the more extraordinary they seem.

Dolphins have large brains and a highly folded cerebral cortex not dissimilar to our own, but it is generally supposed that the bulk of a dolphin's brainpower is devoted to processing acoustic information, for in dolphins hearing and 'language' are extremely sophisticated.

Right: Common dolphins riding the long Pacific swell. Herman Melville, author of Moby Dick, *said of dolphins: 'Their appearance is generally hailed with delight by the mariner. Full of fine spirits, they invariably come from the breezy billows to windward. they are the lads that always live before the wind. They are accounted a lucky omen.'*

A gift for languages

Sound is very important to dolphins. Underwater, where visibility may be poor, sound is a good way of communicating and dolphins have a very varied repertoire of sounds. They make squeaks, whistles, burps, groans, clicks, barks, rattles, chirps, and moans. Some researchers have suggested that there may be an emotional content to some of these utterances. Abrupt, loud sounds, often accompanied by jaw-clapping and tail-slapping, are thought to be a sign of anger. Soft chuckles are heard during bouts of caressing and touching. Whistles seem to be identification signals, each individual having his or her own particular tune.

But dolphin sounds are clearly more than signals or outbursts of emotion. Some researchers believe that dolphins exchange information in a kind of language known as 'delphinese'. In one famous experiment, an American researcher placed a pair of bottlenose dolphins in separate tanks in such a way that they could hear but not see each other. Over a period of time the female was taught to press one of a set of plungers to receive a reward. The male was presented with a similar bank of plungers but had no training. Nevertheless the male very quickly learned to push the correct plunger and the only way he could have received that information was from the female. Throughout the tests the dolphins were heard to emit lots of squeaks, burps, and clicks as if in deep conversation. But the tests were not considered conclusive, for the male might have worked the whole thing out for himself! If he had, that in itself would have been proof of considerable intelligence.

There have been many attempts to teach captive whales and dolphins languages that we humans can make sense of. There have been whistle languages, sign languages, and even high-tech attempts to turn dolphins' ultra-high-frequency utterances into message that we can understand. This has proved difficult

Right: Dolphins seem to enjoy physical contact with humans. Their excellent memory, their powers of mimicry, their ability to invent games and learn tricks, and the complex 'language' they speak to each other all suggest that they are very intelligent, perhaps more intelligent than any other group of animals, with the exception of the primates.

because there is ten times more information in a single dolphin sound than there is in an equivalent human sound. There was even an attempt to teach dolphins English words, but clearly dolphins do not have the vocal apparatus to speak as we do. They are, however, reasonably good mimics and can count up to ten.

The most interesting experiment at present is one being carried out in Hawaii. Bottlenose dolphins are sent this way and that using sign language and sounds, and they appear to be able to understand symbolic words and even sentences. In one set of tests, a trainer stands at the side of the pool and gives arm and hand signals that tell the dolphin to 'throw the frisbee into the bowl' or 'swim through the gate'. The trainer has a blindfold covering his or her eyes. This reduces the likelihood of the trainer inadvertently 'cueing' the dolphin to perform a particular task rather than the dolphin understanding the message contained in the arm and hand signals. The dolphins, it seems, learn very fast.

Seeing with sound

When dolphins are navigating or actively searching for prey, they make very high-frequency click sounds. A school of dolphins will advance in a line, traveling abreast of one another, scanning the sea ahead with bursts of ultrasound. This scanning procedure is called echolocation, and it enables dolphins to 'see' with sound. The sounds emitted by the dolphins bounce off objects in the water and echo back to them, giving them a very accurate idea of the distance, size, and nature of the objects concerned. The way these high-frequency sounds are made is not fully understood, but the principle is one that we too make use of. Aircraft radar operates in a similar way, and modern medicine uses ultrasound as a diagnostic technique to look inside the human body.

Dolphins breathe through their blowhole, which closes when they submerge. The air they breathe is shunted back and forth through a complicated 'plumbing' system, with several vibrating flaps and resonating chambers, to produce high-frequency sounds. These are emitted not through the mouth, but through the forehead. At the front of a dolphin's head is a large bulbous structure known as the 'melon'. Within it are specialized fats which bring the sounds to a focus about 3 feet (1 meter) in front of the dolphin's

head, rather as a camera lens focuses light. The result is a narrow sound beam that can be directed at animate and inanimate objects in the dolphin's path.

The returning sounds are transmitted through the lower jaw, which also contains specialized fatty tissue, to the ear, where they are converted into nerve impulses that travel to the brain for analysis and interpretation. Returning sounds tell the dolphin about obstacles to be avoided or food to be pursued. Not surprisingly, researchers found that fitting rubber suction cups over the eyes of captive dolphins, effectively blindfolding them, made not the slightest difference to their direction – and food-finding capabilities.

'Zapping' prey

When a dolphin is echolocating distant objects, the intensity, or energy content, of the sounds it makes is so great that if they were any louder they would turn into heat! The dolphin is using its echolocation system to the absolute physical limit. Some researchers believe that dolphins use these high-intensity beams of sound to 'zap' their prey. Schools of small fish being chased by dolphins often become disoriented, perhaps because the dolphins 'spray' them with high-intensity sound beams which either knock them out or kill them. All the dolphins then have to do is swim through the fish and gobble them up at will.

Interestingly, dolphins never seem to 'zap' each other, even by accident. With such a dangerous weapon in their heads, they could easily cause unintentional injury. But they appear to have evolved what might be called 'echolocation manners'. If a dolphin is actively echolocating and is approached from the front by another dolphin, it switches off its beam, waits for the other dolphin to swim past, then switches it back on.

Right: In dolphin research programs, scientists are attempting to understand 'delphinese', or dolphin language. Dolphins do not have the vocal apparatus to talk as we do, but they can be taught to understand quite complex arm and hand signals. In dolphin society, sound is a vital means of keeping groups together and coordinating hunting behavior.

Running aground

Occasionally, large numbers of dolphins become stranded on beaches, where they die from overheating. It is strange that such intelligent, expert navigators should get themselves into such difficulties. Some scientists have speculated that parasites in the ear and balance organs might upset their ability to find their way. Others suggest, less plausibly perhaps, that in the sand and mud churned up off beaches or mud flats a dolphin's echolocation system is not much use – soft sand and mud are not the best reflectors of sound. Suddenly finding themselves in very shallow water and unable to see where they are going, they panic, become disoriented, and keep trying to swim onto the shore – even when returned to the water by frustrated human helpers.

Above: Like their larger relatives, the whales, dolphins propel themselves through the water by moving their tail and flukes up and down, the main propulsive stroke being up. The flippers and dorsal fin keep the body on an even keel and offer minimum resistance to water flow. The skin also ripples to reduce 'drag'.

Right: Dolphins are actually small toothed whales, or odontocetes. Their close relatives include orcas and pilot whales, sperm whales, belugas, and narwhals. The teeth are sharp and backward-pointing, well designed for grasping squid or fish, and one set lasts a dolphin for life.

There is, however, another intriguing theory, one involving magnetism. A British researcher, analysing the records of dead or stranded dolphins and whales around the coasts of the British Isles, found that all the single dolphins washed ashore, probably dead due to natural causes, belonged to species that normally live close to land. However, mass strandings nearly always involved species that live offshore in deeper water.

Other research work has shown that dolphins have particles of magnctite (magnetic iron) in their head. These particles are embedded in a dense network of nerve endings and as they respond to the earth's magnetic field they stimulate the nerve endings, sending messages to the brain about the dolphin's position relative to the earth's magnetic field. Other creatures – bees, pigeons, chitons, salamanders – have magnetite in their bodies and it has been shown that changes in the magnetic field can influence the direction in which they travel. Perhaps the stranded dolphins had been swimming along with their echolocation systems switched off, guided by magnetic 'autopilot' as it were, when they hit a 'magnetic valley', a place where the earth's magnetic field is distorted, and became disoriented. Scientists can measure the earth's magnetic field and they have found that the places where mass strandings occur most frequently do indeed coincide with magnetic valleys. Inshore species, used to dealing with the enormous variety of obstacles along a coastline, are probably more careful about where they are heading. Their offshore relatives, with the open, featureless ocean in which to roam, might not be so cautious and so are caught 'napping'.

Below and far right: Divers who swim with dolphins say they can feel a faint tingling sensation on the back of the neck when a dolphin passes by. This may be due to the fact that the dolphin is 'spraying' them with high-intensity sound to find out more about them. In tests, dolphins are able to distinguish between small objects made of different types of metal, even when they are identical in color and shape. They can also discriminate between live fish and dead fish.

Diagram, right: In dolphins, high-frequency clicks are produced by shunting air through flaps and valves just below the blowhole. The clicks are then reflected from the surface of the skull which acts as a parabolic reflector, and directed towards the oil-filled melon in the forehead. The melon acts like a lens, focusing the sound beam in front of the dolphin's head. Incoming sound vibrations are received first by the oil-filled lower jaw and then by the inner ear.

Credit for this theory of sound propagation and reception belongs to the dolphin researcher Kenneth Norris, although not all scientists agree with him.

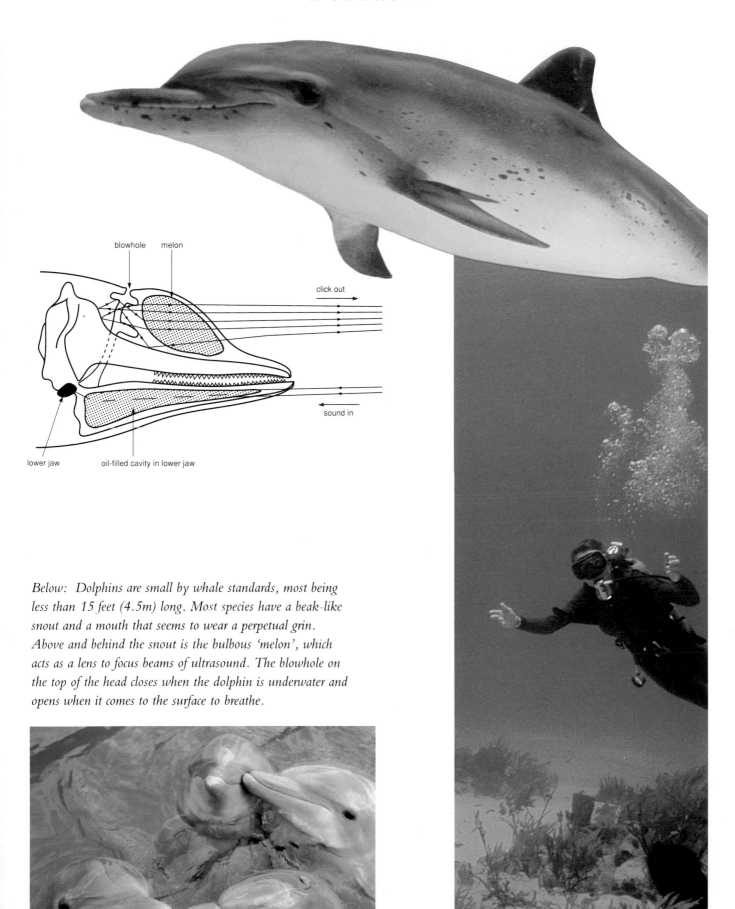

blowhole   melon

click out

sound in

lower jaw   oil-filled cavity in lower jaw

Below: Dolphins are small by whale standards, most being less than 15 feet (4.5m) long. Most species have a beak-like snout and a mouth that seems to wear a perpetual grin. Above and behind the snout is the bulbous 'melon', which acts as a lens to focus beams of ultrasound. The blowhole on the top of the head closes when the dolphin is underwater and opens when it comes to the surface to breathe.

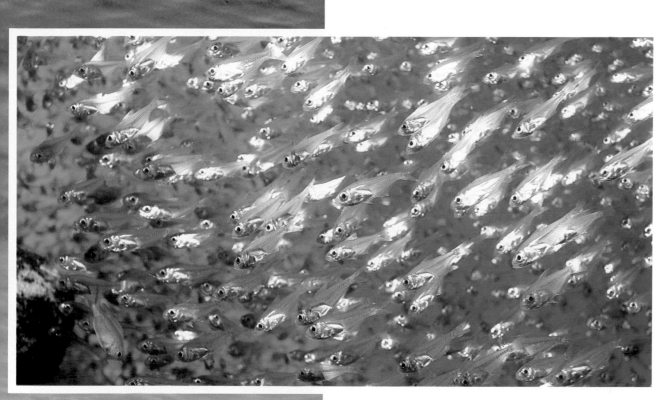

Left and inset: A group of common dolphins 'running' during a hunt. Their prey is a dense shoal of juvenile fish. The dolphins encircle the fish, 'spray' them with sound, and then cut through the shoal, gobbling down as many fish as they can. The fish, whether incapacitated by sound or simply exhausted from the chase, do not attempt to escape. Even large salmon have been seen to stop in their tracks when pursued by orcas (the largest of the dolphins), presumably stunned by high-intensity bursts of ultrasound.

Right and below: Common dolphins breaching off the coast of California. Even in the open ocean, dolphins and porpoises must be wary of obstacles. Every year, abandoned fishing nets floating near the surface of the sea trap and drown thousands of Dall's porpoises. Made of plastic filament, these nets are 'invisible' to dolphin sonar. Monofilament nets, put down for the illegal netting of salmon, are another serious hazard to dolphins and porpoises.

Below right: A common dolphin running, alternately swimming just below the surface and skimming just above it. This very energy-efficient method of swimming allows dolphins to reach speeds of up to 20 miles per hour (35 km/h).

Chapter 6

Adults and youngsters

Over millions of years dolphins have evolved a shape which is near perfect for their underwater existence. They have streamlined bodies devoid of unnecessary projections; they move fast; and they move economically, expending very little energy relative to their size and weight. Even newborn calves swim with great confidence and agility.

As long ago as 1936 Professor Sir James Gray of Cambridge University wrote: 'Nature's design for a dolphin is much more efficient than any submarine or torpedo yet produced by man.' More than half a century later, this is still true. Designers of submarines, torpedoes, and high-speed aircraft have all looked to the dolphin for answers. The dolphin's bulbous head has been copied by supertanker designers, and its body shape has been analysed and incorporated into nuclear submarines.

Speed and stamina

Unlike fishes' tails, which move from side to side, the rear end of a dolphin flexes up and down. The body of a dolphin is not very flexible, although there is some movement in the neck and tail. Most movement occurs at the junction between the tail and the flukes (in whales and dolphins the hind part of the body is the tail and the flukes are an appendage). The dolphin propels itself through the water by means of its tail and flukes only, not by means of its flippers, and can maintain speeds of 10 – 15 miles per hour (16 – 24 km/h) over long distances.

Scientists have devoted much time to understanding this seemingly effortless level of performance, even going so far as to dissect a dolphin's skin and create a rubber model of it. As a dolphin powers through the water, its flexible skin ripples in areas where turbulence occurs, reducing drag. The skin is also ribbed with narrow, transverse ridges rather like the lines of a fingerprint, although the reason for this is not known.

A dolphin's skin is special in other ways too. Whereas human skin has a thick layer of dead cells

A dusky dolphin breaching off the coast of Peninsula Valdès, Argentina. Breaching is a way of spying out the surface of the sea, but if all the dolphins in a hunting group do it, you can be sure they are driving a school of fish in front of them.

above the living tissue, the living cells in a dolphin's skin are close to the surface. These contain droplets of oil which slough off as they reach the skin surface, releasing the oil and lubricating the dolphin's passage through the water. Beneath the skin there is a 1-inch (2.5-cm) layer of fat or blubber. This may be a buoyancy aid rather than a food store or layer of insulation.

Most dolphins are fast swimmers – they have to be in order to catch fish and squid – and they have two distinct swimming styles, cruising and running. A cruising dolphin swims underwater, occasionally breaking surface to breathe. The faster it travels, the closer it gets to the surface and the more frequently it comes up to breathe. At even faster speeds, dolphins begin to 'run', or leap out of the water. At one time, scientists thought that leaping wasted energy, but it has now been discovered that above a certain speed - about 10 miles per hour for a 6-foot (1.8-meter) dolphin - leaping actually saves energy. By alternating shallow dives with leaps about twice the length of their body, dolphins can reach top speed. A running Pacific white-sided dolphin can skid along at 20 miles per hour (32 km/h) in short bursts.

Sometimes dolphins hitch a ride on the bow waves of boats and ships, positioning themselves on the forward slope of the wave like surfriders. Propelled by the force of the water, they actually stop swimming. Dolphins must have sported in this way millions of years before man sailed the seas, riding the bow waves of large whales.

Hunting rituals

Many species of dolphins live in large groups and have daily social routines. Hawaiian spinner dolphins, so-called because of their habit of leaping out of the water and doing double axels in the air, spend most of the day close inshore, apparently resting. In the late afternoon, a few individuals begin to leap and splash about, which seems to be a signal for the rest of the school to rise and shine. The rushing about gets more and more frantic, as if a check is being made on all the individuals in the group to ensure that they are ready to go hunting. The school swims rapidly back and forth a few times, as if to settle who swims next to whom, and

then, at an unknown signal, the whole school turns tail and heads out to sea for a night's hunting.

Dusky dolphins, on the other hand, hunt during the day. They spend the night in small groups close to the shore, swimming slowly at about 3 miles per hour (5 km/h), keeping a lookout for orcas, their main predator. As many as 400 individuals may live in an area only 10 miles (16 km) across, but when they set off hunting they divide into groups of up to 30 individuals.

Each group fans out in a line, scanning the sea ahead for shoals of fish. Occasionally, a dolphin leaps high in the air in order to spot the flocks of seabirds that accompany and feed on large shoals of fish. After 'periscope' leaps like this, the dolphins make a clean re-entry into the water. But when they have located a shoal of fish, they hurl themselves into the air and come down on their side or in a belly-flop, making a terrific noise. This frightens the fish and makes them easier to herd towards the surface of the sea, which acts like a wall, preventing escape. The splashing also brings other dolphin groups to the scene, but whether this is accidental or intentional cooperative behavior is not known. Once they have eaten their fill, spinner dolphins perform amazing acrobatic leaps out of the water, with spins and somersaults. This may be another 'roll-call' ritual designed to bring the hunting groups together again before they retire inshore for the night.

Some species of dolphins have developed associations with other dolphins. Tropical deepwater races of the spinner dolphin, for example, occasionally team up with bridled or spotted dolphins. These are species that live far from land, in the domain ruled by oceanic sharks. At night the spinner dolphins are actively hunting and therefore alert to danger; during the day, it is the turn of the bridled dolphins to hunt and keep watch for sharks. Combined schools can be enormous, with up to 10,000 animals traveling together across many thousands of miles of ocean.

Contrary to popular belief, dolphins can be very aggressive. In some species, fighting establishes the hierarchy, although an open mouth directed at a subordinate can be enough to bring it into line. Teeth marks on subordinates are proof that looks are not always enough!

River dolphins and porpoises

The most primitive dolphins alive today are the river dolphins. These are found in the turbid waters of great river systems like the Amazon, Orinoco, and La Plata in South America and the Ganges, Indus, and Chang Jiang in Asia. Their eyesight is so poor that they rely almost totally on a highly specialized broad-beam sonar to locate food and find their way about. They have long snouts and catch their prey, usually freshwater catfish or crustaceans, in the sharp front teeth and then transfer it to the back teeth for chewing. They are slow swimmers and usually inhabit the quiet sections of rivers where the water is deep and calm. They also tend to be solitary.

Porpoises, similar in shape to dolphins, but without the beak, live in groups of two or three, or alone, and often frequent harbors and inlets. They are smaller than dolphins, generally measuring 4 - 6 feet (1.2 - 1.8 meters) long. One species, the finless porpoise, has no dorsal fin. Porpoises are the most likely large mammals to be found trapped and drowned in monofilament fishing nets - several thousand are killed in this way each year. The fine nets are invisible to their otherwise excellent echolocation system.

A dolphin birth

Like human beings, dolphins are mammals and therefore suckle their young. Although birth and suckling take place underwater, the process has many similarities to our own.

The mother dolphin carries the baby in her womb for nearly a year. About half way through her pregnancy she separates slightly from the rest of her group, but selects a friendly female and spends most of her time in her company. This is the female who will assist her during the birth. Several weeks before the baby is due, the mother starts doing an hour or so of 'prenatal exercises' every day, flexing and arching her body in preparation for the birth.

The baby dolphin, or calf, is born tail first - the birth can take up to two hours, so it is of vital importance that the head and blowhole come out last. Once the calf has emerged, the mother quickly swims around it, severs the umbilical cord, and nudges the calf's head up to the surface where it takes its first

breath. Calves do this automatically within seconds of being born, but the mother is there in case of difficulties.

A newborn dolphin is about 3 feet (1 meter) long, about a third of its mother's length, and weighs about 25 pounds (11 kg). It is born with its eyes open, and is already an agile, confident swimmer. Usually only one calf is born, although cases of twins have been reported.

Within 24 hours the baby takes its first drink of milk. The mother's two milk ducts are located beneath grooves near her tail, so the calf has to dive underneath her to feed. Since dolphins have solid jaws, the calf cannot actually suck the teats, so it wraps its tongue around one of them and this prompts the mother to squirt a large volume of milk into its mouth. In this way the calf gets a lot of nourishment quickly. It then

Above: A bottlenose mother and baby at Windsor Safari Park in England. Europe's first dolphin sperm bank was set up here in 1984 in an attempt to improve the breeding rate in captivity. The U.S. Navy is reported to have trained dolphins to ejaculate on command for a similar captive breeding program. Sexual maturity is reached at 10 – 12 years in males (although male babies practice mating behavior when they are only two or three days old) and at 5 – 12 years in females. Gestation lasts for 12 months. A female bottlenose may have up to eight calves in her lifetime, at two- or three-year intervals.

swims to the surface for air, and returns to the other teat for a repeat performance. At first, the calf feeds every 20 minutes.

Dolphins continue to suckle their young for at least 18 months, far longer than human mothers, although mixed feeding starts at about four or five months, as it does in humans. Dolphin milk is highly nutritious, containing six times as much protein as human milk and much more fat. That is one of the reasons why it takes a baby dolphin only two months to double its birth weight, a process which takes a human baby about six months.

The mother, with the help of other females, protects and assists her calf for several weeks after the birth, keeping sharks away and seeing off any unfriendly males. After that, the young one is on its own, ready to take its place as a member of the group.

Above: Experimental submarines are being built with 'soft' skins to absorb eddies and turbulence; this reduces drag and increases speed and fuel efficiency. A submarine with 'variable streamlining', as it is called, can move 20 per cent faster underwater than a submarine with a conventional hull.

Above and far left: A bottlenose dolphin powers through choppy sea off Newfoundland. Dolphins are such efficient swimmers that designers of submarines have incorporated some of their streamlining into new vessels.

Right: A research dinghy in hot pursuit of a running dolphin. The transverse corrugations that appear in a dolphin's skin when it is swimming fast reduce turbulence and power requirements.

Below: Pacific bottlenose dolphins 'porpoising' off the Galapagos Islands. Pacific bottlenoses are an inshore species, rarely seen more than 500 miles (800 km) from land, and often swim in the company of humpback and pilot whales. They appear to have a set foraging area or home range. On occasions, small sub-groups come together for cooperative feeding, forming large herds of up to 500 individuals.

This page: Just as individual whales can be recognized by the markings on their flippers and flukes, so dolphins can be identified by tears along the trailing edge of the dorsal fin. By photographing dolphin schools, researchers have begun to work out group structure and composition. In a group of 15 dolphins, for example, only five may be permanent members of the group; the others move around from group to group.

If a member of the group is injured or in distress, the others will often show concern, getting very excited, swimming rapidly in circles, biting any lines or nets, or ramming boats. If an injured animal is unable to swim, the rest of the group will gather around and support it so that the blowhole is kept above the surface of the sea.

There are reports of dolphins helping humans in the same way. A 20-year-old girl was saved by dolphins in Delagoa Bay, Mozambique, when she was being pursued by four sharks.

Above: The boutu or *Amazon river dolphin lives in the silt-laden waters of the Amazon basin in South America. River dolphins are generally considered to be more primitive than oceanic dolphins. The* boutu *has poor eyesight, is a slow swimmer, and surfaces frequently, which makes it especially vulnerable to being shot by fishermen who regard it as a competitor for fish. Many* boutus *drown in fishing nets. During the rainy season, when the rivers of Amazonia burst their banks,* boutus *swim deep into the forest in the shallow flood water.*

Left: A dusky dolphin breaching off Peninsula Valdès, Argentina. Dusky dolphins are an inshore species, distributed around the coasts of South America, South Africa, southern Australia, and New Zealand. A captive dusky dolphin in a marine circus in New Zealand immediately went to the aid of a diver pretending to be in distress.

Below: A school of common dolphins porpoising off the coast of California. Common dolphins are found worldwide in temperate and tropical waters, both inshore and offshore. The species is fished illegally in the Black Sea, but the main threat oceanwide comes from gill nets and purse-seine nets.

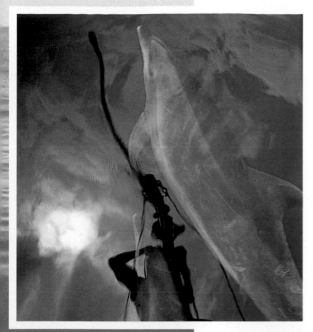

This page: Dolphins are expert riders on ships' bow waves. Positioning themselves on the downslope of the wave, they stop swimming, and surf along at speeds of up to 35 miles per hour (56 km/h). One New Zealand common dolphin traveled for 70 miles (113 km) like this before veering off. Bottlenose dolphins sometimes bodysurf on waves close to the beach, turning back as the waves just begin to break.

Any object moving through the water creates a pressure wave in front of it. Young dolphins sometimes travel in front of their mothers in order to take advantage of this free energy.

Chapter 7

Performance with a smile

One of the first marine aquaria to specialize in keeping and training dolphins to perform in public was Marineland of Florida at St. Augustine. Initially the facilities were used to make underwater films, but the dolphins quickly took center stage and Marine Studios became Marineland, one of the most successful dolphinaria in the world. Millions of people have been entertained there by the tricks and antics of dolphins and small whales.

However, Marineland of Florida was not the first establishment to exhibit dolphins. During the nineteenth century many zoos and aquaria in Europe held captive dolphins and porpoises. Some even tried to exhibit whales – several belugas were taken to Britain in 1897, but they died. Indeed, survival in captivity has been a constant and serious problem for dolphinaria. Wild animals seem to live much longer than captive animals, and breeding in captivity, except in a few key centers, is proving difficult. Many zoos and aquaria have had dolphin births, but few young dolphins survive to maturity.

The first breeding group of dolphins, bottlenose dolphins, was established at Marineland of Florida. Bottlenoses have proved to be the most successful species in captivity. However, many of the dolphins in zoos and oceanaria around the world are taken from the wild, and conservationists are very critical of such establishments.

Nevertheless, dolphinaria have provided marvellous opportunities for observing dolphin behavior. Marineland of Florida pioneered early research into the sounds that dolphins make for communication and echolocation. It was here, in the process of testing the theory that dolphins can find their way about without using their eyes, that researchers realized how hard it is to blindfold a dolphin! Nothing would stay attached to the dolphin's head and nothing would stick to the skin. Researchers at Marineland of the Pacific in California found the solution: they put rubber suction cups over the dolphin's eyes and these stayed in place, even while the animal swam at great speed in the tank.

The bottlenose TV star

The first dolphin to take part in tests was named Kathy. She was a bottlenose dolphin partly trained at Marineland of Florida, and it was through her that scientists began to understand some of the extraordinary sonic abilities of dolphins.

Kathy demonstrated her skills thanks to the CBS-TV science-based show *Conquest*. Keeping and experimenting with dolphins is a costly business, so CBS filmed the project for one of its broadcasts. Kathy was trained in the same way as other performing dolphins. First she learned, by repetition, that a peep from a whistle meant that she had carried out a simple task correctly and would receive a morsel of fish as a reward. Then she was taught more complicated maneuvers, starting with a simple trick and gradually building this up into a much more elaborate performance.

Kathy's first blindfold test was to locate a target panel, press a paddle which caused a bell to ring, and then return to the researcher for her reward. This she quickly achieved. Underwater microphones in the tank confirmed that Kathy was using sound to find her way to and from the target, even when the target was only 1 inch (2.5 cm) across and she was 12 yards (10.6 meters) away from it. Small pieces of fish, dropped in

the water, were easily found and hastily gobbled down. A maze of vertically placed rods was negotiated with ease – the blindfolded Kathy did not touch a single rod, even though the configuration of the maze was constantly changed.

Dolphins have incredible memories for tricks and are amazing mimics. One researcher even had a dolphin that mimicked human words, sounding rather like a parrot, and counted up to ten.

Back-flips and feathers

Sometimes, the tricks that dolphins do are self-taught and they like an appreciative audience. At the Oceanic Institute of Hawaii a dolphin suddenly performed a new trick; when it was rewarded, it responded with back-flips, somersaults, and splashes, and even swam upside down with its tail high in the air! A pair of dolphins in another tank invented a game with a large white feather. They found that if they placed the feather in the current of water from the inlet pipe, it would shoot across the pool and they could chase and catch it. Soon they discovered that if they placed the feather in the eddies to the side of the main current they could beat it across the pool.

Dolphins in captivity can be 'moody' and are quick

to become bored. A trainer must be extremely sensitive to these moods, for an uncooperative dolphin can be very awkward indeed. If a dolphin is fed up with repeating a trick over and over again, it will sulk at the side of the pool or splash the trainer and anyone else within splashing distance.

Performing dolphins also have their own ideas about their routines. At Seaworld in San Diego, a trainer cut short an orca's performance and the orca promptly dragged her into the water by her leg. The crowd rose in horror, expecting her to be ripped apart, but her leg was hardly scratched. It was the only way the orca could make its protest.

Status and security

Observers of captive dolphins suggest that a dominance hierarchy exists in dolphin groups. The dominant male in a tank prefers to swim at the center or near to the clean water inlet. He also tends to swim alone, occasionally accompanied by a female or younger male, and sometimes shows signs of aggression. When a

young male approaches the female companion of a dominant male, or heads towards a choice piece of food, he is seen off with a bite to the body or a slap with the tail, a very gentle reprimand when you consider that a dolphin can knock the stuffing out of a shark by ramming it with its snout.

At Marineland of Florida, the second highest-ranking dolphin was a female named Pudgy. She was not at all in awe of the dominant male, but rather inquisitive about him. If any strange diver entered the tank, she viewed him as a potential threat, even if he was wearing exactly the same underwater suit and breathing equipment as the regular keeper. Pudgy would inspect him and, providing she judged him to be friendly, would report back to the dominant male who would then venture forward to make his own inspection.

Left and below: Using simple verbal, visual, or whistle commands and a fishy morsel as a reward, dolphins can be taught to perform the most amazing tricks, even leaping through hoops of fire. But sometimes a dolphin will sulk or get angry, and refuse to carry out a trick or splash water over the trainer.

Dolphins released back into the wild are often reluctant to take their freedom. Those that have lived with humans for any length of time seem to find it difficult to break the tie and fend for themselves again. Understandably so, for their natural behavior has been substantially modified. At Marineland of Florida, for instance, a dolphin was released into the Atlantic, but it stayed close to the aquarium site for several weeks before it finally swam off. A few days later a dolphin was caught just a few miles away - it seemed to want to get caught. At the Aquarium of St. Petersburg Beach on the Gulf coast of Florida, another newly released dolphin kept turning up in fishing nets in a series of attempts to get back to its tank. The people at the aquarium eventually gave in and let it return, much to the relief of the local fishermen.

Unfortunately, dolphins in captivity have suffered illness and even death as a result of human malice or plain stupidity. At Windsor Safari Park in Britain, for instance, a ball studded with nails was found floating in the dolphin pool. In the same pool a dolphin died after eating a plastic bag.

Dolphins today are valuable animals. Dolphinaria, particularly in the United States, are big business, and the stars do not come cheap – it is not just bottlenose dolphins that perform there but also white-sided dolphins, belugas, pilot whales, false killer whales, and even enormous orcas. Many millions of dollars change hands in the process of procuring these animals from the wild.

Above: Pacific white-sided dolphins in high spirits at San Diego, California. These dolphins are such good jumpers that they have been known to land on the decks of boats.

Above: Pacific white-sided dolphins have a less pronounced beak than other species. Schools of white-sided dolphins may number thousands of individuals. The species occurs throughout the Pacific Ocean, and there is a similar form in the Atlantic.

Left and below: Dolphins learn their tricks step by step, mastering simple routines first, then building up to longer, more complex stunts. Fish are the usual reward, although dolphins also seem to find an intrinsic satisfaction in displaying their acrobatic skills, often behaving as if they are very pleased with themselves.

This page: Most captive dolphins enjoy physical contact with trainers and visitors, often popping out of the water for a scratch or flipper shake. Even more remarkable was the behavior of Beaky, a wild bottlenose dolphin who frequented the south coast of England in the 1970s. He appeared to be able to distinguish between men and women: toward men, he was friendly, but as soon as they touched him, he would start to behave as a dominant male; toward women who touched him, his behavior was overtly sexual.

Below: Who is studying whom? Dolphins are intelligent enough to invent their own games. On one occasion, a pair of bottlenoses took an interest in a moray eel in their tank, but the eel quickly became tired of their antics and retired into a rocky crevice. Not satisfied, the dolphins caught a spiny scorpionfish and encouraged it to swim into the crevice. The eel made a quick exit, and the dophins began their game all over again. In the wild, dolphins have been seen playing with pieces of fish and strands of seaweed.

Left: Dolphins in captivity are affected by work and social pressures. Three overstressed dolphins at Baltimore aquarium – Aphrodite, Mimi, and Kibby – were sent to Florida for rest and recuperation. They were not asked to perform tricks and were not involved in social status battles in their tank, but the gaze of 1.6 million visitors a year proved too much for them – they developed gastric ulcers.

Chapter 8

Fiction and fact

Dolphins have fascinated us since prehistoric times. In caves in South Africa there are primitive works of art depicting men swimming with dolphins. In Ancient Greece and Rome artists commonly portrayed dolphins on cups, plates, medallions, furniture, frescoes, and coins. No fewer than forty Greek city states used the image of a dolphin on their coinage.

The Greeks also invented an explanation for the mutual affinity between dolphins and people. The young and beautiful Dionysos, the god of wine and frenzy, was sailing to Naxos one day when it occurred to him that the crew were taking the ship to Asia with the intention of selling him as a slave. So he filled the ship with vines, conjured up a band of invisible flutes, and transformed the crew's oars into serpents. The men, quite understandably horrified, leapt into the sea, where they were turned into dolphins by Poseidon, the god of the sea. Dolphins, as transformed and reformed pirates, are now quite friendly to people....

Another legendary Greek, Telemachus, the son of Odysseus, was given proof of this friendship. As a child he fell into the sea and was on the verge of drowning when a dolphin rescued him. Thereafter, Odysseus wore a ring engraved with a dolphin and had another emblazoned on his shield.

Dolphins to the rescue

Stories of people being rescued by dolphins abound in early literature. The Greek historian Herodotus, for example, writing in the fifth century BC, relates that

Common dolphins traveling in line abreast. For many centuries, seafarers in the Mediterranean regarded the presence of dolphins as a good omen; when the dolphins disappeared, a storm was brewing. The sailors of ancient Crete caught and tamed dolphins, and often hung fish from the prow of their ships to attract dolphins as pilots. A dolphin-god is said to have guided the first worshippers to Delphi, sanctuary of Apollo and center of the world.

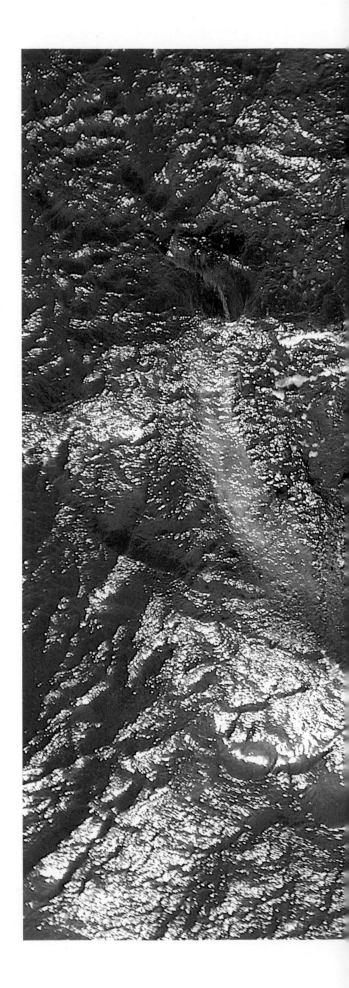

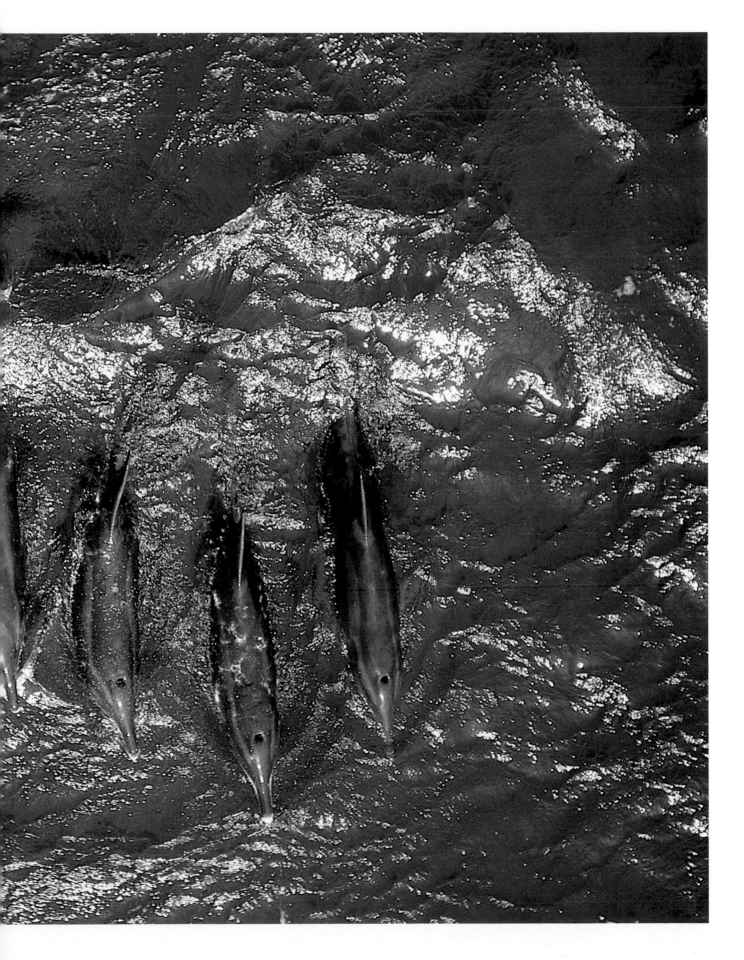

the poet Arion was saved by a dolphin. The incident occurred when Arion was on his way back from Sicily, having won a poetry competition. The sailors on the ship, taking a fancy to the rich prizes he had won, decided to get rid of him, but just as they were about to push him overboard, Arion asked to be allowed to play his cythara, or lute, one last time. His wish was granted, and he struck up a high-pitched song that attracted a group of dolphins to the ship's side. His song over, he was thrown into the sea and left to drown. But he survived. One of the dolphins carried him on its back to safety.

But reports of dolphin rescues are not just fiction. Many have appeared in modern newspapers. Fairly recently, four fishermen from Cape Town, fishing off the Cape Peninsula, were suddenly enveloped in a fog so thick they could hardly see their hands in front of them. They were aware that their ship was drifting toward dangerous rocks, but were unsure which way safety lay. Suddenly a small group of dolphins appeared, the fishermen followed them, and found themselves guided into a sheltered anchorage. During World War II, a rubber dinghy containing six American airmen was pushed ashore by dolphins in the Pacific. And in 1966 dolphins fought off sharks and helped a bather to reach the shore in the Gulf of Suez.

There is the story, told by the head trainer at a marine circus in New Zealand, of a captive dusky dolphin responding immediately to a diver pretending to be drowning. The dolphin lifted him up and held him above the surface at the side of the pool. The same dolphin also went to the aid of the sick baby of a common dolphin in the same tank.

Dolphins certainly help each other; indeed, this must be the basis of their concern for people. There are many recorded instances of dolphins supporting a sick or injured companion, keeping its head at the surface so that it can breathe. Dolphins have also bitten through harpoon lines to release a speared companion, and charged boats when one of their number has been caught. Among Russian fishermen, there is even the tale of a group of dolphins protecting a seal from a pack of orcas.

Naval dolphins

The U.S. Navy has been training dolphins and pilot whales to recover warheads and other hardware lost on the bottom of the sea, and it is generally known that the navies of several countries are currently training dolphins (or have done so in the past) to fix explosives to the hulls of enemy vessels, find or destroy enemy mines, or detect the presence of enemy submarines. If dolphins can be trained to do all this, it is not too fanciful to imagine them taking part in front-line attacks, perhaps exploding underwater mines - and killing themselves in the process - or guarding harbor entrances against enemy frogmen.

But since military research is conducted in great secrecy, little specific information is available. We do know, however, that dolphins were used to patrol harbor installations during the Vietnam and Iran-Iraq wars, although it is not certain what part they played in hostilities. The public outcry may have acted as a deterrent to the use of such peaceable animals for naval warfare. On the other hand, experiments may still be continuing, in yet greater secrecy....

Below and inset: Dolphins involved in military activities are trained to live freely in the sea yet return to their base on the command of their trainer. Tuffy, a U.S. Navy-trained bottlenose, liaised between laboratories on the seabed, Sealabs II and III, and their surface ship. He also guided lost divers back to their submarine bases.

Researchers at Batumi on the Black Sea, USSR, are investigating the possibility of setting up a dolphin dairy farm, since dolphin milk contains many times more fat and protein than cow's milk.

One for you, one for me!

Between Cape Blanc and Cape Timiris, on the coast of
Mauretania in Africa, live the Imragen people.
Conditions are hard in this part of the world, and the
Imragen rely on fish in times when other food is scarce.
They catch migrating shoals of mullet with the aid of
dolphins. Naturally, the dolphins are also there to catch
the mullet. As they see the dolphins appear on the
horizon, the fishermen place their nets in the shallows
offshore, the dolphins drive the mullet into the nets,
grabbing as many fish as they can swallow and
sometimes diving between and around the legs of the
fishermen, and then leave. The Imragen haul out the
fish that are left and dry them in the sun. To the
Imragen, the dolphin is a sacred animal.

In Burma there are similar instances of cooperation
between dolphins and people – at various times, several
villages have had an obliging local dolphin. On the
Tepegos River in South America, a explorer once saw
a fisherman using an Amazon river dolphin to help him
catch fish. The fisherman would tap the side of his boat
with an oar and whistle a strange tune, and the dolphin
would appear. Then, as the fisherman drove the fish
toward the river bank in his boat, the dolphin
frightened them to the surface. Both man and dolphin
did very well out of the arrangement.

In the first century AD the Roman historian Pliny
the Elder wrote about French fishermen using dolphins
to find shoals of fish. The dolphins were rewarded
with a share of the catch and pieces of bread dipped
in red wine.

Protected dolphins

In many parts of the world there have been reports of
individual dolphins repeatedly turning up at the same
place. Such a dolphin was Pelorus Jack, a Risso's
dolphin that lived in the Cook Strait between the
North and South Islands of New Zealand. Pelorus Jack

would greet steamships and leap about in front of the bows, as if guiding them through the strait. Pelorus Jack became a tourist attraction, and the New Zealand government passed a Special Order in Council making it illegal 'to take fish or mammal, commonly known as Risso's dolphin, in the waters of Cook Strait'.

Any dolphin caught in British waters automatically belongs to the Crown. An act passed in 1320 states that all dolphins, whales, and sturgeons must be offered for the Royal Table or allowed to swim free in the seas. Even an injured animal that has been patched up in an animal hospital must be given its freedom when fully recovered. Without special permission from the Crown, it is illegal to keep a dolphin caught in British waters.

Above and inset: A 'superseiner' catching tuna and a Dall's porpoise trapped in a 'superseiner' net. The biggest threats to Dall's porpoise – porpoises are smaller than dolphins and lack a beak – are the salmon drift nets of the Japanese Salmon Fisheries Cooperative that operates, under permit, inside the U.S. Fisheries conservation zone and is allowed an 'accidental' take of more than 5,000 dolphins and porpoises a year.

Unnecessary slaughter

Despite all this seemingly intelligent and cooperative behavior, dolphins are caught and killed in their thousands. Dolphins in the Pacific Ocean, for example, swim with the tuna - the same tuna that end up in cans in the supermarket. In fact, tuna fishermen look for leaping dolphins to tell them where the tuna are. The tuna are caught in huge purse-seine nets, and as the strings of the 'purse' are drawn in, the dolphins are trapped along with the tuna.

Legislation has been introduced in the United States to minimize the number of dolphins killed in this way. When the nets are hauled in, one side must be temporarily slackened to let the dolphins escape over the top. Another law passed in 1972 forbids the capturing or importing of marine mammals into the United States. Products made from marine mammals are also forbidden. And yet 40,000 dolphins are still killed each year.

Perhaps the greatest slaughter occurs around the Japanese island of Iki, where the fishermen claim that they are competing with the dolphins for valuable fish. Thousands of dolphins are trapped, hauled out of the water by their tails, knifed or clubbed to death, and then fed into grinding and mincing machines that turn them into pig-fodder. Iki Bay turns red with their blood.

The Japanese authorities tried to frighten the dolphins away with the aid of an artificial killer whale that emitted threatening noises, but the dolphins weren't fooled. But in this case, their intelligence cost them their lives.

How to assist stranded dolphins

● Keep the skin wet. Dolphins breathe air and can survive for several hours out of water as long as their skin does not dry out.

● If a dolphin is exhausted, don't put it into deep water. It may be too exhausted to swim and could therefore drown. Support it in shallow water with the blowhole just covered, allowing the animal to bend its head up to breathe. Although dolphins can be very heavy – some weigh up to 800 pounds (360 kg) – it does not require phenomenal strength to do this.

● When several dolphins are stranded together, moving one back into the water at a time will not work. A rescued dolphin will instinctively return to join its stranded companions. The solution is to summon enough help to move all the dolphins back into the water at the same time. If this is impossible, try moving some higher up the beach and then move one out into the water. If its companions are sufficiently far away, their whistles of distress will not travel through the water and summon it back. You can then move the others down one at a time.

● You will have to handle a dolphin firmly, but try to be gentle. Dolphins do not like having their flippers yanked, but these, and their tail flukes, are really all you can get hold of. Be calm and deliberate, and the dolphin will not panic. A dolphin is more likely to die from struggling than from being out of the water. But remember, KEEP THE SKIN WET AT ALL TIMES.

Right and inset: Dolphins being trapped and slaughtered at Iki, Japan. Hundreds of dolphins are herded into the harbor at Katsumoto and killed because the local fishermen feel that their livelihood is threatened by the dolphins eating or chasing away the fish. Conservationists worldwide have condemned this slaughter. An American who released a herd of dolphins trapped by the fishermen of Iki received a suspended prison sentence.

Left: The head of a common or harbor porpoise, a North Atlantic costal species. Harbor porpoise numbers are in decline, possibly due to pollution, disturbance, or conflict with fisheries.

Below: In 1979, at Izu in Japan, 6,000 dolphins were slaughtered to supply the teriyaki (grilled meat) market. In 1980, when environmentalists announced that the meat was contaminated with ten times the level of mercury allowed for human consumption, the price dropped drastically and the slaughter was reduced.

*Left and above: A diver pretending to be in distress receives playful assistance from a bottlenose.
Wild dolphins, particularly bottlenoses, like to frolic with fishermen and bathers, even nudging
swimmers in difficulty towards the safety of the beach. In the 1970s, one particular bottlenose
became well known around the coast of Britain. Nicknamed Donald in the Isle of Man, Bubbles
in Wales, and Beaky in Cornwall, his favorite playmates were women and children.*

Left: The sad sight of stranded dolphins. Although partly explained by the 'magnetic valley' theory, strandings are still puzzling in an animal as intelligent as the dolphin. In some respects, dolphins are still mysterious, but as Plutarch wrote in the first century AD: 'To the dolphin alone nature has given that which the best philosophers seek: friendship for no advantage. Though it has no need of help of any man, yet it is a genial friend to all, and has helped man.'

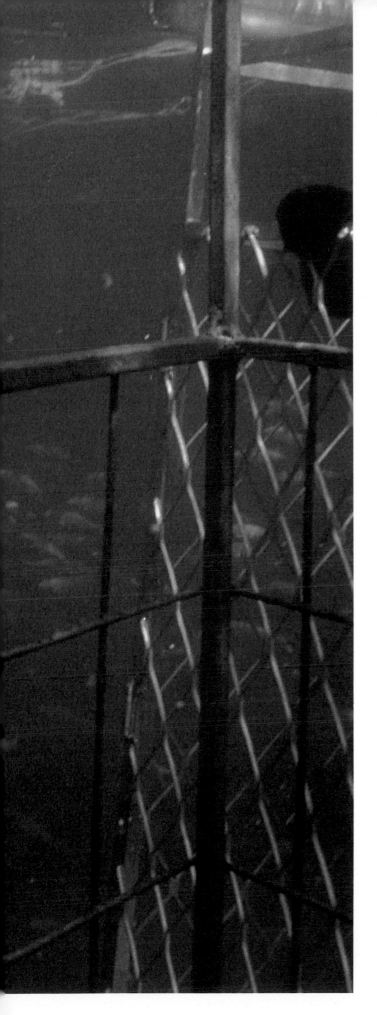

Chapter 9

Making headlines

On Sunday, July 24, 1983, the 40-foot (12-meter) fishing trawler *New Venture* foundered off the Great Barrier Reef in Queensland, Australia. A boom broke, the boat heeled over, was hit by a freak wave, and turned turtle, throwing the 28-year-old skipper Ray Boundy and his crew, 21-year-old cook Linda Horton and 24-year-old Dennis 'Smurf' Murphy, into the water.

'Smurf was on deck and jumped straight into the water', recalled Boundy, 'but Lindy and I were caught in the wheelhouse. We all ended up sitting on top of the upturned hull wondering what on earth we were going to do.'

The trawler began to sink, and the three laughed and joked about their chances of survival as they grasped one life ring, three large pieces of foam, and a surfboard to keep themselves afloat. They were confident that they would be spotted and rescued.

On the evening of the next day a shark appeared – a 15-foot (4.5-meter) tiger shark. It circled them, nudged the life ring and the pieces of foam, but didn't attack. 'We weren't worried' said Boundy, 'because I'd seen sharks before. We weren't taking much notice of him, thinking that if we didn't antagonize him he might, with a bit of luck, leave us alone.'

But the shark didn't leave them alone. It disappeared below the surfboard and came up to take a bite at Boundy's knee. 'I panicked a bit and jammed my other foot down on him and he just let go. I said to Smurf: "We're not ready to be his dinner just yet." '

Five minutes later another large wave knocked the trio off their flimsy rafts and into the sea. The shark grabbed Smurf's leg.

'Next thing, my mate was screaming his head off', continued Boundy. 'Smurf said: "He's got my leg, the

Left: A great white shark investigates a diver's safety cage, curious about the sounds and movements coming from inside it.

shark's got my leg." Then he said: "I've lost my leg", and the shark pulled him under a couple of times. I could see the blood coming to the surface through the water. I didn't know what to do. "Kick him as hard as you can" I yelled.'

The shark came back and began to close in.

'Smurf did the bravest thing I have ever seen. He tried to swim away from us toward the shark to divert it, calling back to us: "You and Lindy bolt, because he'll come back for the rest of me." When I turned round I saw the shark finish him off. As it picked up the top of his body and dived, Smurf was just screaming. I couldn't believe that anyone could have that much guts to try and get his mates out of trouble.'

Linda became hysterical, but Boundy was able to calm her down. For a couple of hours they made good headway, paddling towards the edge of Loaders Reef, which they estimated they would reach by morning. But the shark returned.

'Lindy was sitting in the sling of the life ring with her feet up on the foam and I was holding her hand when I saw him come along again. He slewed around and grabbed Lindy around the arms and chest.

'I was still holding her hand as he shook her about three or four times, just like a rag doll, causing the life ring to fall off. She only let out one little squeal, as soon as it hit, and I knew that she was dead. She didn't know what had happened.'

Using pieces of foam, Boundy paddled as fast as he could toward the reef. Just after daybreak, the shark reappeared.

'It was just going round and round me. I had lost my two best friends and now the shark had come for me.'

Every time the shark came close, Boundy stopped paddling and let himself drift until it had gone. At last he could see the reef. At this point a spotter plane flew overhead.

'I knew I'd be all right if I could just make the reef. I waited until the shark disappeared and used the foam to surf over the reef edge. I was 100 yards off the reef, and the shark had followed me. It was still zigzagging along behind me.'

Boundy caught a wave and was taken over the reef. He scrambled ashore, laughing hysterically. Then it all hit him and he broke down and cried.

Primeval fears

Ray Boundy's tragedy was undoubtedly one of the most horrific shipwreck and shark attack stories in Australian history, yet it it was almost a re-run of an incident in Moreton Bay, 10 miles (16 km) to the north of Brisbane, in March 1977 when three fishermen were thrown into the water after a freighter had sliced their boat in two. For 36 hours the men clung to a floating icebox, but just 45 minutes before their rescue the sharks arrived. Small ones bit at their bodies, and the blood and the commotion attracted a 19 1/2-foot (6-meter) great white shark, known locally as a white pointer. Two of the fishermen were killed and one survived by climbing into the icebox.

Both stories quickly became front page news in Australian newspapers, were widely covered on radio and television, and were reported in considerable detail in newspapers all over the world. They had touched that primeval fear most of us have of 'creatures from the deep', of sharks in particular. Psychiatrists suggest that this is a fear which goes right back to the time when our ancestors left the shelter of the forest and faced the threat of being eaten alive by the great savannah and grassland predators.

Sharks terrify and fascinate us in a way that no other dangerous animals do, not even lions or tigers. Few divers who have looked up and suddenly faced those unblinking, black, expressionless eyes and mouth ragged with rows of serrated teeth would argue with that.

What, who, and when?

In reality, of the 350 or so recognized species of sharks, only 30 have been known to attack human beings. Of those, the great white, the tiger, the hammerhead, the bull, the gray nurse, the oceanic whitetip, the mako, and the blacktip top the record for causing deaths and casualties. However, most of them find human flesh unpalatable and readily spit us out! In general, sharks are not man-eaters but man-attackers, a subtlety understandably lost on most victims of shark attacks.

'Swimmers Dash From Sea In Shark Panic', 'Beach Terror As Shark Eats Man', and 'Jaws! Hunt For Suspect Killer Shark' - headlines like these underline our morbid fascination with shark attacks. Yet road accidents during just one holiday weekend kill more people than have been killed by sharks, worldwide, in the last ten years. The majority of attacks are by sharks less then 6 1/2 feet (2 meters) long.

It has often been suggested that the water temperature must be at least 70°F (21°C) for there to be a risk of shark attack. Only 14 percent of bathers questioned at Siesta Keys in Florida felt tempted to swim when the water was below 70°F (21°C). Swimmers in other parts of the world may be more or less hardy but, generally speaking, most swimming occurs in relatively warm water. It may be our behavior that governs the pattern of shark attacks rather than the other way around.

How a shark attacks

A shark attack is usually quick and terrible. When a shark attacks it use all of its finely tuned senses – sophisticated senses are the hallmark of most successful predators.

A shark can smell blood or body fluids from about 1/3 mile (0.5 km) away; these form an 'olfactory corridor' which it follows upcurrent towards its victim. From about 150 yards (140 meters) away, it can hear and accurately locate the low-frequency sounds of commotion in the water. At 25 yards (22 meters) away – and even when it is almost dark – it can see the movement of its prey. Then, as it closes in to attack,

Above and left: This is how the Australian papers reported the shark attack on Ray Boundy, captain of the New Venture, *and his crew in 1983.*

another sense takes over, one that detects minute electric currents.

As the shark nears its target a special protective membrane, a nictitating membrane, flicks over the eyes, so for the last few seconds of its attack run the shark is essentially swimming blind, relying on the electrical information detected by nerve endings located in small pits all over its snout. The more frantic the muscle movements of the target, the stronger the currents created in the water.

Although a shark's bite is powerful, the main damage is inflicted by the shearing action of the teeth. A shark has an endless conveyor belt of teeth, which are probably replaced about five times a year.

A shark's hydrodynamic efficiency is partly due to its body shape but also to the nature of its skin, which is covered with tiny tooth-like projections, or dermal denticles. These trap mucus secreted by the skin, producing a surface which offers the least possible resistance to water flow. In the mackerel sharks, the group to which the great white and the mako belong, swimming speed is increased by keeping the immensely powerful swimming muscles a few degrees warmer than the surrounding seawater.

According to one shark expert, there are two recognizable patterns of shark attack. 'The first is a quiet approach, where the shark will almost casually grab the victim and produce a severe wound, shake the person around a little bit and then leave. The other is more violent, when the shark will strike repeatedly in a frenzied fashion, producing severe wounds. Death of the victim is the likely outcome of the struggle.'

When sharks do decide to attack humans, nowhere on the beach is safe. Attacks can occur in any depth of water, even paddling depth, but the risk of shark attack increases as you move further from the shore. The deeper the water, the further you venture into the shark's domain...and the further you are from help.

More case histories

• On Rivera Beach, Florida, in August 1966, an eight-year-old boy and his mother were paddling in about 12 inches (30 cm) of water when a shark charged at the boy. His mother whisked him away in the nick of time and the shark, carried on by its own momentum, ended up on the sand, where it thrashed about until a wave washed it back into the water. Curiously, as the mother and the boy walked along the shoreline, well clear of the water, several sharks followed them.

• A group of sharks had congregated around a fisherman who was gutting and washing his morning's catch at the water's edge. A tourist skindiver, out to prove his manhood, harpooned one of them. The animal went berserk. It swam rapidly away, breaking the line, shook the harpoon out, and then returned to the beach. It leapt out of the water, tried to grab the skindiver, failed, and returned to the sea on the next wave.

• In April 1990, off Greenmount Beach in Queensland, Australia, a surfer escaped with cuts and bruises when an enormous chunk of his surfboard was chomped by a 10-foot (3-meter) tiger shark. Four days previously another surfer survived an attack in the same area.

• In May 1990, on Australia's Great Barrier Reef, two snorkellers were savaged by a 6-foot (2-meter) hammerhead shark, and two sneaker-clad feet were found in the stomach of a shark caught off Mayport on the Atlantic coast of Florida.

• In June 1990, a 21-year-old woman was killed by a great white shark in Mossel Bay, South Africa.

• In September 1990, in California, a canoeist paddling just 10 yards (9 meters) away from the shore was knocked out of his craft by a great white, grabbed around the shoulders, and then spat out. He got back into his canoe and paddled rapidly for the shore.

• In October 1990, in Australia, a 27-year-old swimmer struggled from a Queensland saltwater canal and crawled to a nearby house after an attack by a shark. It was the second attack in the same canal within a year. Later, a 6-foot (2-meter) bronze whaler shark was caught.

Right: The savagery and unpredictability of great white attacks was epitomized in the film Jaws *and its sequels.*

Left: Tigers sharks are second only to great whites in their record of attacks on humans. They are powerful but leisurely swimmers and eat almost everything — seabirds, molluscs, crustaceans, turtles, fish, seals, dolphins, and garbage.

Left: Survivors of Australian great white shark attacks examine the huge bites taken out of a shark by other great whites. Henri Bource (on the right and also below) lost his leg twice in great white attacks — first his real leg and then his artificial one!

Right: An undaunted Henri Bource doing what he likes most: diving to watch sharks.

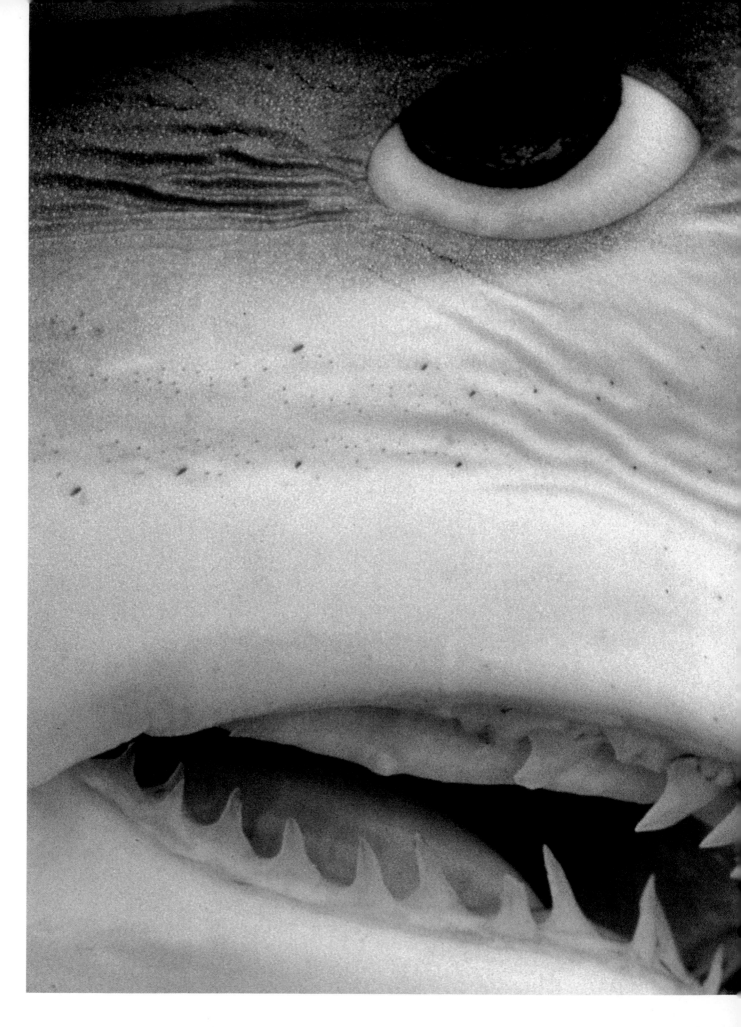

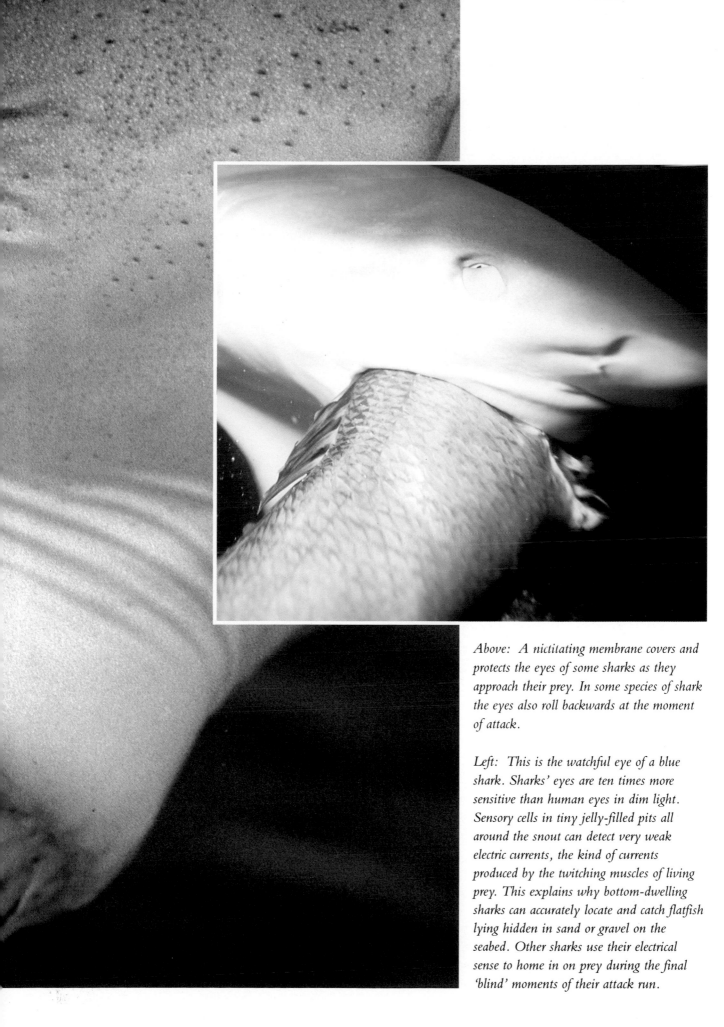

Above: A nictitating membrane covers and protects the eyes of some sharks as they approach their prey. In some species of shark the eyes also roll backwards at the moment of attack.

Left: This is the watchful eye of a blue shark. Sharks' eyes are ten times more sensitive than human eyes in dim light. Sensory cells in tiny jelly-filled pits all around the snout can detect very weak electric currents, the kind of currents produced by the twitching muscles of living prey. This explains why bottom-dwelling sharks can accurately locate and catch flatfish lying hidden in sand or gravel on the seabed. Other sharks use their electrical sense to home in on prey during the final 'blind' moments of their attack run.

This page: Great whites seem to be attracted by the small galvanic currents produced in seawater by the metal bars and floats of shark cages and outboard motors. Much to the consternation of skindivers and crew members, they often ignore bait meat and repeatedly attack and try to bite these metal structures, often driving themselves into a frenzy. The metal fittings on scuba diving equipment are attractive to sharks for the same reason.

Below: A shark can detect blood and body fluids from a potential victim at least a quarter of a mile (0.5 km) downcurrent. The ensuing encounter may result in the shark going beserk in a 'feeding frenzy'. Water is drawn into the nostrils and the chemicals in the water stimulate olfactory nerve endings inside the nasal capsule. In starving sharks, the sense of smell becomes even more acute than normal.

Above: *From the side, the bonnethead shark looks like any other shark. But it belongs to the hammerhead family and the eyes are set wide apart on the 'wings' of the semicircular head. The advantages of a head like this may be a better appreciation of distance, as the shark swings its head from side to side, or a greater surface area on the snout for electroreceptors.*

Left: *In hammerhead sharks, the mouth is set under the head at the point where the head joins the body. Most species of hammerhead are tropical and feed on fish and stingrays.*

Right and far right: A great white shark being 'teased' with baits of horsemeat off Dangerous Reef, South Australia. Great whites are fast, agile, and powerful swimmmers. Their torpedo shape and huge flattened tail are hydrodynamically near-perfect. The blood vessels that supply the powerful swimming muscles are arranged in a 'heat exchanger' configuration to conserve heat. This enables the shark to maintain its muscles at a temperature a few degrees above that of the surrounding water.

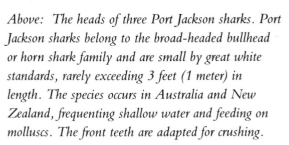

Above: The heads of three Port Jackson sharks. Port Jackson sharks belong to the broad-headed bullhead or horn shark family and are small by great white standards, rarely exceeding 3 feet (1 meter) in length. The species occurs in Australia and New Zealand, frequenting shallow water and feeding on molluscs. The front teeth are adapted for crushing.

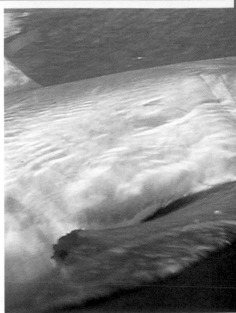

Left: *When a great white attacks a large item of prey, the jaws are protruded forward so that the bite can be delivered straight ahead rather than as a sideways swipe. A great white can cram 100 pounds (45 kg) of food into its stomach at one meal, which will last it three months.*

Below left· The top and bottom teeth of the great white are triangular and serrated. Interestingly, young great white sharks feed mainly on fish and have teeth shaped more like those of the mako (on the left). It is only when they are older and considerably bigger that they develop a full set of teeth for tearing chunks out of seals or whales.

The teeth of the mako shark are more pointed than those of the great white, for impaling fish. In most sharks the teeth are on a 'conveyor belt', with new teeth continually forming behind those currently in use. Some sharks have just one row of teeth, others several rows, but in all species the teeth are constantly shed. The replacement rate for lemon sharks, for example, is one tooth every eight days! A single shark may produce thousands of teeth during its lifetime.

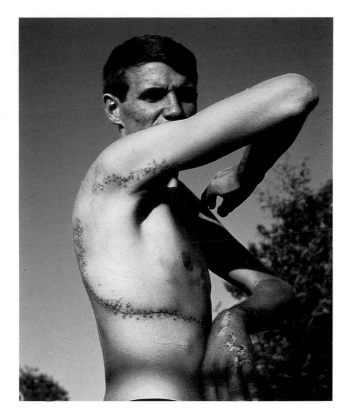

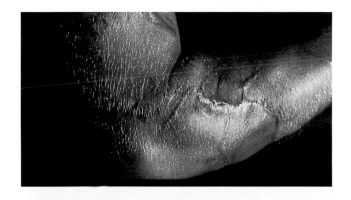

Above, left and below: Often the species of shark is identified by the teeth it leaves behind, or by the size and shape of the wounds. The majority of shark attacks on humans involve only one bite or slash, which had led some shark experts to conclude that most attacks are not motivated by hunger. Some victims who have survived attacks by large sharks remember being picked up, shaken like rag dolls, and then spat out.

Even a shark brushing past a swimmer can result in serious abrasions, since the shark's skin is covered with tiny tooth-like projections.

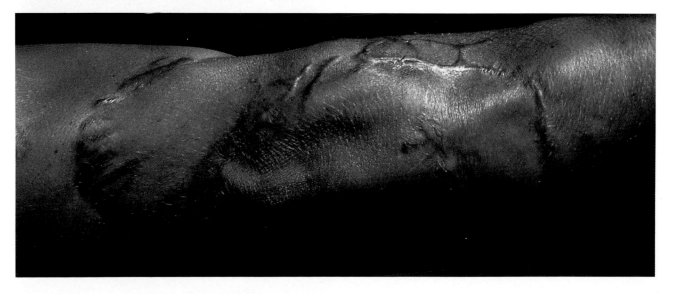

Above: The whitetip reef shark is common around coral reefs and islands in the Indian and Pacific Oceans. It is a sluggish species, largely nocturnal in habit, and feeds on fish and invertebrates. It grows to a length of about 6 ¹/₂ feet (2 meters).

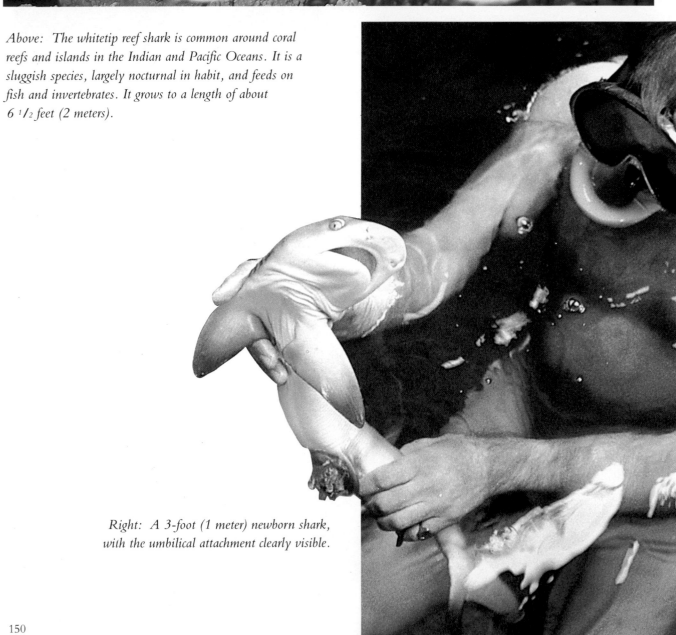

Right: A 3-foot (1 meter) newborn shark, with the umbilical attachment clearly visible.

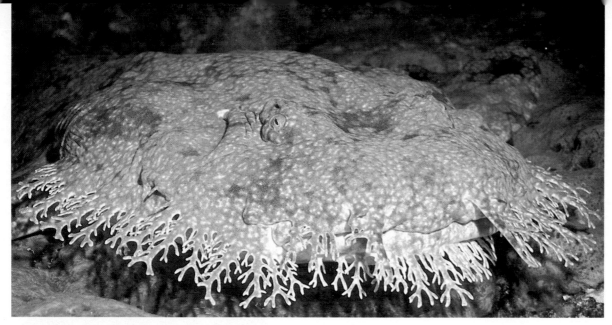

Above: A well camouflaged wobbegong shark waits for lunch. You can see the slit of the right eye and the bump over the left. Now and then it twitches its fringed appendages to simulate wafting seaweed. There are eight species of wobbegong (an Australian aboriginal name), all of them shallow-water bottom-feeders restricted to the Western Pacific. Size varies from 1 1/2 – 10 feet (0.5 – 3 meters), the carpet shark being the largest species. Despite their sluggishness, wobbegongs have been known to attack humans in retaliation for being speared or trodden on.

Left: This is the broad-snouted outline of a bull shark, a member of the 90-strong genus sometimes referred to as requiem sharks. It is the only shark to have cracked the problem of existing in brackish and fresh water – there are populations in tropical estuaries, rivers, and even in Lake Nicaragua. In South Africa, most bull shark attacks on humans occur between December and March, when the species congregates in estuaries to scavange food brought down by rivers in spate.

Below: Swell sharks are able to inflate themselves with air or water to deter potential predators. There are seven species of swell sharks, all of them tropical and conspicuously patterned.

Chapter 10

Mighty white

All over the world the great white shark has become a sinister celebrity thanks to Peter Benchley's film *Jaws*. Great whites attack anything, at any time, and without warning. The only predictable thing about great whites is their unpredictability.

Great whites do not usually eat their human victims. After the initial bite, the victim is often released – survival depends on whether any major arteries have been severed and how quickly help arrives. One interpretation of this 'maiming' behavior is that the shark is waiting for the person to bleed to death before returning and eating him or her.

Great whites are unusual in that they venture into temperate waters. In summer, it seems, the giant mature females make their way to the waters off the New England coast of the United States to give birth to their pups. The most northerly attack along this coast occurred at Buzzard's Bay, Massachusetts, in July 1936. A swimmer in water only 10 feet (3 meters) deep was attacked by a great white. He was rescued, but died later in hospital.

The most gruesome series of attacks along the New England coast took place a great deal earlier. In July 1916, during World War I, when many thousands of soldiers were being slaughtered in Europe, five attacks in ten days made front page news. All of them happened along the coast of New Jersey. Perhaps the most horrific was described by David Baldridge in his fascinating book *Shark Attack*: 'One of the boys dived from a piling into the murky water and, after having felt something rough grate across his midsection, clambered from the water to find his stomach streaked with blood. He cautioned his friends, "Don't dive in any more – there's a shark or something in there!" But soon he too ignored even his own warning by again

A great white uses its shearing teeth to rip away the head of a horse being used as bait. The jaws can close with a pressure of 20 tons per square inch (3 tonnes/cm^2) and the teeth have the same hardness as steel.

diving into the creek. Some time later, 12-year-old Lester Sitwell called to a friend who was about to climb out of the water: "Watch me float, fellas!"

'As the other boy turned to watch Lester, he felt something slam against his leg and looked down to see what appeared to be the tail of a huge fish. It was heading straight for his friend. Young Sitwell screamed and in an instant was pulled down into the dark depths of Matawan Creek.... The creek became crowded with would-be rescuers, some in boats and others diving into the murky water not yet fully realizing what had happened and the fate that possibly awaited them just below the surface of the creek.'

One brave would-be rescuer, Stanley Fisher, dived several times into a deeper section of the creek. A stain of blood appeared around him and, according to one report, he emerged from the water holding his severed right leg above his head. He died later in hospital.

Several sharks were caught near the creek, but attention focused on an 8 1/2-foot (2.6-meter) great white which was found to have about 15 1/2 pounds (7 kg) of human flesh, a boy's shin bone, and a rib bone in its stomach.

Above: This is the 5-inch (12.5-cm) fossil tooth of Carcharodon megalodon, *a shark that lived several million years ago. Shark experts, comparing these teeth with the teeth and jaws of living relatives, estimate that megalodon's body length must have been at least 43 feet (13 meters). Could megalodon still be living and breeding somewhere in the ocean depths today? 'Living fossils' such as coelocanths, once thought to have died out millions of years ago, suggest that we should not be too dogmatic about such creatures being extinct.*

Left: Sharks can turn cannibals. This great white, hooked by a sports fisherman, has been savaged by other great whites. Uterine cannibalism is well documented in sand tiger sharks, which give birth to live young, the embryonic sharks inside the mother attacking and killing each other until only the fiercest and fittest are left. A marine biologist who thrust his hand inside a freshly dissected 8-foot (2.5-meter) female sand tiger shark was promptly bitten on the thumb by a 3-foot (1-meter) youngster lurking inside her.

Right: A great white takes an experimental bite at a makeshift raft. Despite its name, the great white is slaty gray, dark gray, or blue above; only the belly is cream, dirty white, or pale gray. There is usually a black spot where the pectoral fins join the belly.

Above: Great whites do not always attack suitable items of prey. Sometimes they just investigate, as here. In fact, pioneer underwater explorer Jacques Cousteau, diving off the Cape Verde Islands, once encountered a great white that took fright: 'His reaction was the least conceivable one. In pure fright, the monster voided a cloud of excrement and departed at an incredible speed.'

Left: Henri Bource poses with a great white caught off South Australia. It has been suggested that great whites live for up to 50 years, becoming sexually mature at around 10 years. The young are thought to be about 3 feet (1 meter) long at birth.

This page: Great white sharks at Dangerous Reef, South Australia, being attracted to 'rubby-dubby' slicks of mashed up guts and blood near the diving boat. Having homed in on the source of the smell, the sharks are induced to 'perform' in front of the movie camera with the aid of chunks of horsemeat. Feeding a great white by hand is a hazardous business. There is always the possibility that the shark will turn on the flimsy cage and rip it apart.

Although silent themselves, sharks use sound to help them locate their prey. A struggling fish or a sick seal makes low frequency sounds that are highly interesting to a shark. Experiments with underwater loudspeakers have shown that many species of shark can be attracted within minutes to sounds in the 25 – 50 Hz range, at the lower end of human hearing. One researcher also noticed that the throbbing sounds of helicopter rotor blades attract sharks – not a reassuring thought if you are being rescued by helicopter from shark-infested waters. The sounds of a lone swimmer thrashing about in the water also attract sharks.

Far right: A spear fishermen kills a great white shark using a harpoon with an explosive head.

Right: The trophy is brought ashore, but such indiscriminate slaughter may already have brought the great white to the brink of extinction in South Australian waters.

Below: A sand tiger shark (known in Australia as the gray nurse shark) with a remora attached to its belly. Remoras have a suction disk (a highly modified dorsal fin) on top of their head for attaching themselves to sharks and other large fish. The remora gets a free ride and first refusal of any fragments of food that spill from the shark's mouth, but the shark gets nothing. Sand tiger sharks occur in most shallow tropical and subtropical waters throughout the world, but not in the Eastern Pacific.

Far right: Beauty and the Beast? Australian skindiver Valerie Taylor, with her husband Ron, has taken some of the most exciting film footage of great white sharks. The movie Blue Water, White Death, *made in 1971 with Stan Waterman and Peter Gimbel, includes sequences of three huge great whites at Dangerous Reef.*

Right: A great white approaches the stern of the Taylors' diving boat but ignores the bait and instead attacks the metal diving platform. Was it confused by the electric currents given off by the metal, or was it more interested in Valerie Taylor's feet!

Below: Great white jaws, removed from the head, cleaned, and mounted, fetch at least US $1,000 on the tourist market.

Chapter 11

Dangerous waters

The greatest number of attacks by great white sharks in the United States has occurred in a triangular stretch of the Pacific Ocean bounded by Monterey in the south, Point Reyes in the north, and the Farallon Islands in the west. This area is known, ominously, as the 'Red Triangle' and the increase in shark activity in recent years seems to coincide with the successful conservation of another giant sea creature, the northern elephant seal.

By the early 1970s, the intensively hunted elephant seal was on the brink of extinction, so a ban was imposed on hunting. The seals recolonized their traditional breeding sites and the population began to recover. The conservation scientists were very pleased... and so were the great white sharks.

Great whites congregate near the breeding beaches and lie in wait for the seals as they return to breed. The gigantic bull elephant seals, the largest of all the seals – up to 16 feet (5 meters) long and weighing 5,000 pounds (2,270 kg) – are their favorite targets.

An expectant gathering of western gulls over a patch of sea is the giveaway. The shark slams into its enormous victim, the water turns red with blood, and the waiting gulls gobble up the fragments of flesh sprayed into the air by the ferocity of the attack.

The shark approaches the seal from below and behind, choosing areas where the bottom is rocky. Seen from above, the shark's dark body shape matches the color of the rocks. If the seal spots the shark and takes evasive action at the last minute, the tremendous momentum of the shark's attack run propels it clean out of the water.

This technique of hunting seals from below may explain some of the attacks that have been made on swimmers and surfers along this part of the East Coast.

A diver's view of the perfect torpedo shape of a gray reef shark. Much photographed around the reefs of Australia and the Western Pacific, gray reef sharks are one of the few large species of shark in which mating behavior has been observed.

From below, a swimmer on the surface or a surfer on a surfboard looks remarkably like a seal behaving strangely. To any hungry predator, a familiar shape behaving in a strange way, in a way that suggests it is sick or injured, is an open invitation. The fact that great white shark attacks on humans take place in areas where there are seal or sealion colonies suggests that humans are not the primary targets. They are, from the shark's point of view, aberrant seals.

Moving with the seasons

One of the most important factors affecting the distribution of sharks, both dangerous and harmless, is water temperature. Along the coast of the northeastern United States, to the north of Cape Hatteras in North Carolina, a recognizable pattern of shark movements takes place during spring and early summer. An 'Apex Predator' tagging program, in which scientists and sports fishermen have cooperated to catch, label, and release sharks, has revealed that the 68.5°F (20°C) isotherm – an imaginary line linking places where the seawater is at this temperature – is an important factor in shark distribution in this part of the world. Isotherms change their position according to the time of year.

In May and early June, blue sharks move inshore, over the continental shelf, from their deepwater wintering areas in the Sargasso Sea and along the north wall of the Gulf Stream off Bermuda, ahead of the 68.5° F (20° C) isotherm. They prefer cool water. Mako sharks and swordfish stay just behind this temperature boundary, which means that they reach the northeast coast somewhat later, in late June and July. Hammerhead and tiger sharks prefer slightly warmer water. In the fall, all of these species move south into deeper water, following retreating temperature boundaries.

At this time of year, blue sharks split into two groups: the large males stay in the Western Atlantic, while the females make their way to the coasts of Europe, the Azores, and Africa, following the clockwise movement of the North Atlantic Gyre.

Cape Hatteras, which juts far out into the Gulf Stream, forms a divide between the water masses to the north and south of it. To the north, there are quite large seasonal variations in sea temperature; to the south, the sea temperature is relatively constant throughout the year. Along the Florida coast, hammerheads and tiger sharks are to be found all year round.

European waters

Several potentially dangerous sharks share the favorite resorts of European holidaymakers. The thresher shark and two first cousins of the great white, the mako and porbeagle, frequent the south and southwest coast of Britain and the English Channel, and there are great whites in the Mediterranean and Eastern Atlantic.

In December 1979, off the northern coast of Madeira, southeast of the Azores, a swimmer was killed by a great white, the first such attack in the island's history. Around the Azores themselves, when open-boat whaling was a thriving local industry, many large great whites would congregate around the whaling boats, taking chunks out of the dead sperm whales they had in tow.

But the largest great whites ever seen in European waters – mostly females, which grow much larger than the males – have turned up in the Mediterranean. Could some parts of the Mediterranean be great white pupping sites? In April 1987, a 23-foot (7-meter) female, one of the largest ever landed, was caught off the island of Malta. And in the same year two more females were found entangled in nets near the Egadi Islands off the west coast of Sicily. In 1983, there was a shark scare in the Aegean and in 1985 another along the coast of Italy, near Anzio.

The thresher shark has an enormous scythe-shaped tail, and has been known to approach small craft along the south coast of England and in the Bay of Biscay. In June 1981, a thresher almost 13 feet (4 meters) long hurled itself into a 23-foot (7-meter) boat filled with anglers fishing of the Isle of Wight. 'It turned towards the boat and dived,' recalled one of the fisherman. 'Everything was quiet...then there was a great rushing noise and suddenly the shark came out of the water about 15 feet (4.5 meters) away. It landed across the boat and the impact nearly sank us, but it killed the shark outright!'

Nevertheless, shark attacks in British waters have been few. One occurred near Wick in Scotland, when a fisherman was mauled. Another happened at Folkestone on the Kent coast, when two children were swept off their feet by the long tail of a thresher. At Swanage in Dorset two anglers were trapped against the rocks by three angry threshers - throughout July 1981 there were large numbers of threshers in the area, chasing a superabundance of mackerel and scaring bathers from beaches around Bournemouth and Christchurch. At Beesands, in south Devon, a mako shark went for a lone skindiver not far from the beach.

Another incident occurred in 1972 on the Manacles Reef in Cornwall. Several scuba divers were exploring the reef. As they reached the surface, their leader, from his vantage point on the support boat, spotted trouble. 'I noticed that two divers had already surfaced and were giving what seemed to be a distress signal. I noticed that a shark's fin was circling the two divers, so I said to the skipper of the boat: "We'd better pick those two up." He said: "No boy, don't worry about it, it's only a basking shark." But I could see that the two were definitely agitated and were giving very firm distress signals.

'When we reached them they were back to back with knives out, and the shark was circling them intently. We got the boat between the shark and the divers, lifted the diving set off one of the divers and helped him aboard. Suddenly the shark stopped circling, faced the other diver and came forward rapidly. I shouted to the others to get the chap on board and we lifted him bodily, equipment and all, clear of the water. At the same time the shark swam under the boat at the point where the diver had only a couple of seconds before been floating in the water. That was the last we saw of the shark.'

Anti-shark measures

How can we protect ourselves from shark attack? Most research into shark defense has been done in the United States, South Africa, and Australia.

One of the most effective ways of protecting a popular bathing beach from sharks is 'meshing', a method used in South Africa and Australia. The meshing consists of two parallel rows of nets, with floats at the top and weights at the bottom, strung across the beach just beyond the line of the surf. The rows are not continuous, for outer nets alternate with inner nets. This arrangement allows sharks to pass through as they head for shallower water, but catches them on the way

out. Their heads get caught in the nets, and without any forward motion to keep water flowing through their gills, they asphyxiate and drown. Sharks tend to come into shallow water at night. At dawn, they move out and are caught. Over a relatively short period, the number of sharks in the vicinity is reduced to the point where the probability of attack is very small. In Australia, no attacks have occurred at meshed beaches. Of course, if anyone is foolish enough to enter a meshed area for a night swim....

An ingenious personal shark survival aid developed in the United States consists of a plastic bag folded up to the size of a pack of cigarettes. It is called the Johnson Shark Screen. Swimmers and divers carry it with them when they are in the water. If you are attacked, you open the bag and climb into it. It then fills with water and submerges, but is kept afloat by inflatable rings around the top. Any blood or other fluids likely to attract a shark stay inside the bag.

Then there is the Shark Shield, still in the early stages of development, a device that takes advantage of the shark's ability to sense electric currents in the water. It delivers a fairly weak DC current that can barely be felt with the hand but which will ward off a shark.

Various chemical deterrents have been considered. One which seems promising is a toxin derived from the Moses sole, a flatfish found in the Red Sea. Sharks find the milky fluid it exudes from the base of its fins extremely repugnant. In tests in the United States two captive sharks were given a Moses sole to eat, and the result was instant lockjaw! They took the fish into their mouths, but were unable to complete their bite. The Moses sole toxin had paralyzed their jaws. So it has been suggested that a slow-release version of the toxin, incorporated into neoprene diving suits or contained in a fast-acting 'shaving stick' device on the end of a 'shark billy', might be developed to protect commercial divers.

Tests continue. Until an effective deterrent is found, caution is the best protection. When swimming in water known to be frequented by dangerous sharks, take care, or that swim may be the last you take.

THE TOP TEN KILLERS

1 Great white shark

Grouped with the the porbeagle and mako as a mackerel shark, the great white is the largest and most powerful predatory fish in the sea. It is found in all oceans, at all latitudes, and is considered to be one of the most dangerous creatures on earth. It can grow to a length of 30 feet (9 meters), although the average is 15 – 16 feet (4.5 – 4.9 meters), which means a weight of about 3,000 pounds (1,360 kg).

Most great whites are found close to sea mammal colonies along the coasts of California, South Africa, and South Australia. Along the northeast coast of the United States, great whites are attracted by the carcasses of large whales. Most attacks on humans have been cases of mistaken identity – great whites really do prefer seals.

2 Tiger Shark

This large and aggressive species, known to exceed 20 feet (7 meters) in length, makes attacks in tropical and subtropical waters worldwide. Easily recognized by its broad head and prominent nostril flaps, its long-lobed upper tail fin, and the striped pattern on the sides of younger individuals, it is the most feared shark in the Caribbean and the islands of the South Pacific.

3 Bull sharks

These belong to a group of sharks found inshore in tropical and subtropical parts of the world, particularly in the fresh or brackish waters of Lake Nicaragua, the Amazon, Zambesi, Ganges, and other rivers throughout Africa, Asia, and Australasia. Bull sharks are thought to be responsible for the majority of attack on swimmers along South African beaches and have even been known to attack young hippos.

4 Oceanic whitetip shark

This very common and very powerful oceanic species turns up in large numbers when there are disasters at sea. It is characterized by white fin tips, long pectoral fins, and the retinue of pilot fish that often swims in front of its snout. Whitetips occur all over the world and can grow to a length of 12 feet (3.6 meters).

5 Whaler sharks

These belong to a group of recognized 'mankillers', and include the blue, black, and bronze whaler.

They are intermediate in size – about 12 feet (3.6 meters) long – and are responsible for many attacks in Australian waters, particularly along the Great Barrier Reef.

6 Hammerhead sharks

Hammerheads, with their unmistakable head and reduced pectoral fins, occur in most tropical and subtropical waters and are considered dangerous. The wide 'hammer' probably allows a very wide angle of vision because the eyes are so far apart, as well as a greater area for electrical sensors. The largest species grow up to 20 feet (6 meters) long.

7 Blue shark

This very common, elegantly streamlined species, with its long pectoral fins, grows up to 12 feet (3.6 meters) long. It is found in warm and temperate waters all over the world. Fast and maneuverable, it is often seen near rotting whale carcasses and has a habit of turning up after shipwrecks, searching for scraps of food.

8 Blacktip reef shark

This modest-sized shark (2 – 5 feet/1.5 meters long) occurs in shallow waters in the Indian and Pacific Oceans. Watch out for small individuals when wading waist-deep! Many attacks have been by individuals barely 2 feet (0.6 meter) long – size is no guide to aggressiveness.

9 Gray reef shark

This is a tropical inshore species whose aggressive behavior may be prompted by defense of territory. When it arches its back, drops its pectoral fins, and swims in a pronounced weaving pattern, back off as quickly as possible! Its next action will be to attack with mouth wide open.

10 Sand tiger sharks

This group of sharks, sometimes known as ragged-tooths on account of their mouthful of fang-like teeth, is found in the coastal waters of Australia, South Africa, North and South America, Japan, China, and India, and is also known in the Mediterranean. In American waters sand tiger sharks are considered harmless; elsewhere they are given a wide berth.

Above: The blacktip reef shark is found in southwestern parts of the Pacific, and in the Indian Ocean, the Red Sea, and the Mediterranean. It appears to be spreading westward, but has not yet reached the Atlantic. Between 4 and 14 pups are born, with gestation taking 12 – 16 months.

Left: Female hammerhead sharks often congregate in large numbers by day, in resting 'refuges', particularly around coral formations in the Gulf of California, the Gulf of Mexico, and along Florida's Atlantic coast. At night they disperse and go hunting. Hammerheads have a special muscle – rather like the elevator in an aircraft's tail – that enables them to move their head up and down.

Right: Porbeagle sharks, first cousins of the great white, occur in cold and temperate waters more or less worldwide. In summer, they can be caught off the southwest and southern coast of Britain. The largest ever caught in these waters was 8 feet 4 inches (2.5 meters) long. Porbeagle steaks, marinated in white wine, are considered a delicacy in France.

Inset: The common thresher shark is an Atlantic species. It often comes close inshore during the summer, chasing shoals of mackerel, which it rounds up with its long scythe-like tail. Various observers have seen threshers hunting in small groups.

Above: The jaws of a captured mako shark, showing the many rows of fang-like, fish-trapping teeth. Even around British coasts, makos weighing up to 400 pounds (170 kg) have been recorded. Although tolerant of cooler waters, makos generally prefer tropical waters. Makos are fast and aggressive, and sometimes make spectacular leaps into the air when hooked, even landing on the decks of fishing boats.

Above and left: The whale shark is the largest known fish in the sea. It is harmless, feeding on the vast quantities of microscopic animals that float in the upper layers of the ocean. It can grow to a length of 40 – 50 feet (12 – 15 meters), and is characterized by rows of white dots all over the body.

Whale sharks are thought to give birth to 'live' young. One youngster, a tiny replica of an adult, was found in a fish market in Oman; it had a fresh 'umbilical' scar, indicating that it had been born rather than hatched from an egg. Until this discovery, it was thought that whale sharks laid eggs. An egg case looking very much like a giant version of the dogfish's 'mermaid's purse' – an extraordinary 27 x 16 inches (68 x 40 cm) – was once dredged up from the seabed near Port Isabel, Texas, but this may have been aborted by the mother. Normally, the eggs develop inside the mother's body until the youngsters are large enough to lead an independent life.

Above: A blue shark bites into a bait fish. Blue sharks are of modest size by great white standards, although large males can grow to 12 feet (3.5 meters). Note the nictitating membrane covering the eye as the shark delivers its bite.

Above: The blue shark is one of the most elegant of sharks, with a pointed snout and long, slender pectoral fins. It is a bright indigo blue above and pale on the belly. Female blue sharks have specially thick skin on their backs to withstand the bites of mating males. Mating takes place in summer and the female stores the sperm until the following spring, when she ovulates. The pups, up to 100 of them, are born in spring the following year.

Right: Sports fishermen and scientists have undertaken a cooperative program to tag blue sharks in an attempt to ascertain their numbers, seasonal movements, and details of their biology. As a result of this work, it has been found that blue sharks make tremendous migrations around the North Atlantic, following the North Atlantic Gyre in a clockwise fashion. However, only the females make the journey, the larger males staying off America's East Coast. Females tagged off Long Island have been recaught in the English Channel, the Mediterranean, and the Azores.

Below: A basking shark is brought alongside. Basking sharks grow to a length of 30 feet (9 meters) or more but are relatively harmless, although the powerful tail can easily capsize a small boat. Although generally sluggish, basking sharks have been known to leap clear of the water, perhaps in order to dislodge parasites.

A basking shark towing a transmitter was recently tracked from a space satellite in an attempt to find out where basking sharks spend the winter. Scientists now think that they hibernate on the seabed in deep water, during which time they molt their gill rakers.

Left: A blue shark takes a snack from a diver. See how the upper jaw moves forward under the snout as the shark bites

Left: Lemon sharks occasionally fall foul of bathers because they frequent tropical, shallow water. Adults are about 10 feet (3 meters) long, but heavily built and sluggish. Like many other species of shark, they are most active at night.

Left: A snooze after dinner... or before dinner?

Below: The dorsal fin of a bull shark slices quietly through the waters of Table Bay, South Africa. Most shark attacks in this part of the world are by bull sharks.

During a seven-year period over 7,000 sharks were meshed off South African beaches; 600 of them were bull sharks, 300 were tiger sharks and great whites, and the rest were makos, lemon sharks, and ragged tooths. There are very few shark attacks off other African coasts.

Right: A dummy diver is prepared for initial tests on a 'chain mail' diving suit.

Far right: Another test for the 'chain mail' suit, this time for real. The testee is a large sand tiger (gray nurse) shark

Left: A diver fends off an aggressive shark with a 'shark billy'. The charge in the end of the weapon explodes when it comes into contact with the shark, killing it.

Right: Diver Valerie Taylor, clad in a protective 'chain mail' diving suit, tempts a shark shark to bite her. The suit is effective against small sharks, but would provide little protection or peace of mind against the huge teeth and jaws of a great white (below).

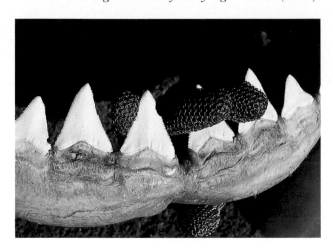

Above: A hammerhead firmly meshed in a net protecting a bathing beach. Many beaches in South Africa and Australia are protected by 'meshing'. Sharks can only swim forward, so once their head becomes trapped they are immobilized and die of asphyxiation.

Right: A meshed shark is retrieved by a meshing boat off Sydney, New South Wales. Australia has the most dangerous waters in the world as far as sharks are concerned, followed by the United States and South Africa.

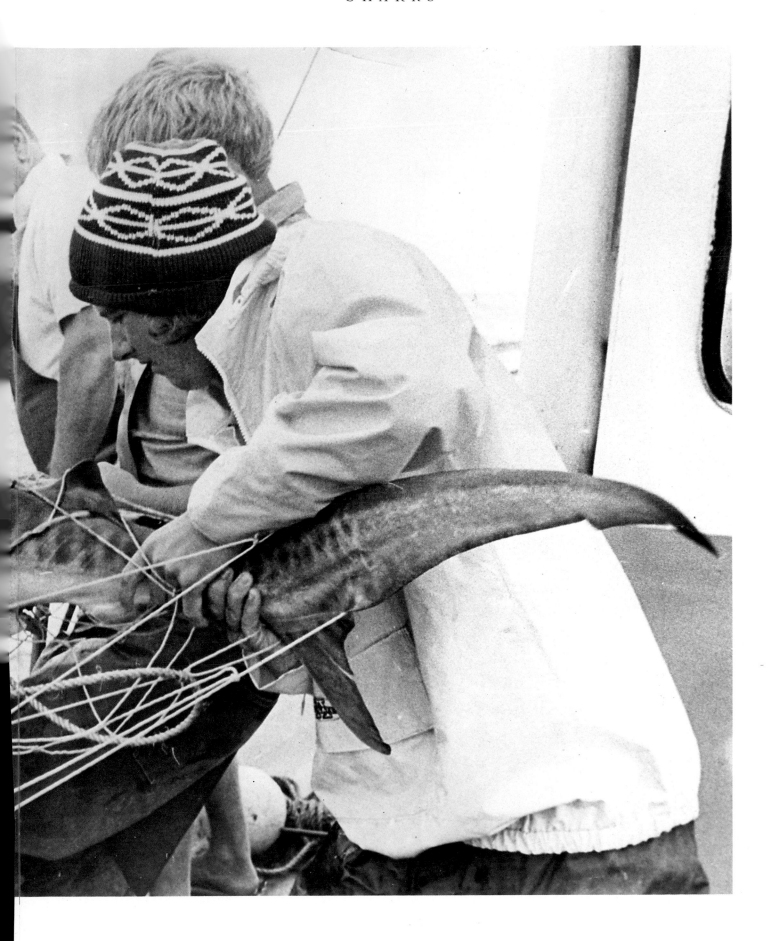

Advice for bathers and swimmers

● Always swim with a companion, and do not drift away from other bathers. A solitary swimmer is a prime target for attack.

● Do not swim in water known to be frequented by dangerous sharks. Leave the water if sharks have been sighted or are thought to be in the area.

● Although not conclusively proved, it is thought that human blood attracts and excites sharks. Keep out of the water if you have open wounds or sores. Women should avoid swimming in the sea during menstruation.

● Avoid swimming in murky or turbid water, where underwater visibility is poor. Keep your eyes open for shadows and movements in the water. If you are in any doubt, get out!

● Do not swim a long way out from the shore - the deeper the water, the higher the probability of encountering a shark.

● Avoid swimming alongside channels or dropoffs to deeper water – these provide sharks with ready access to shallower water.

● Leave the water if there are unusual numbers of fish about and/or if they are behaving in an erratic manner.

● Seeing porpoises around does NOT mean that there are no sharks in the area.

● Choose dark-colored rather than brightly-colored swimwear when swimming in shark areas.

● Avoid uneven tanning of the skin – sharks apparently respond to discontinuities in shading.

● Do not swim with an animal such as a dog or a horse.

● Look around carefully before jumping or diving into the sea from a boat.

● Particularly at low tide, take a good look at nearby sandbars or reefs where sharks may be trapped.

● Avoid swimming at dusk or at night – these are the times when sharks are known to search for food.

● Never, in any form or fashion, molest a shark, no matter how small it is or how harmless it might appear.

Advice for divers

● NEVER DIVE ALONE. The very presence of another diver can deter a shark, and together you have a better chance of spotting a nearby shark and taking effective action. Also, if something does happen, assistance is close at hand.

● Do not keep captured fish, dead or alive, about your person or tethered to you on a stringer or similar device. Remove all speared or wounded fish from the water immediately.

● Choose your wetsuit color carefully - you don't want to be mistaken for the natural prey of sharks in the area.

● Do not spear fish in the same vicinity for too long or sharks may be attracted by your quick movements or by an accumulation of body fluids from the fish you have caught.

● If you see a shark of reasonable size, even if it appears to be minding its own business, leave the water as soon as possible. Use smooth swimming strokes, making no undue commotion, as you make for the safety of a boat or the shore. To the greatest extent possible, remain submerged, where your chances of watching the shark's movements and countering an attack are greater. Do NOT count on the shark circling or passing close at hand without contact before it makes a direct run. It may come straight for you.

● Carry a shark billy or plan to use the butt of a speargun to keep an aggressive or curious shark at bay.

● Take full advantage of your submerged position and limits of visibility to spot nearby movements and presences. Shark attack case histories indicate that such vigilance has been a major factor in minimizing injuries and reducing mortality rates among diver-victims.

● Never maneuver a shark into a trapped position between yourself and an obstacle such as a beach, reef, sandbar, or even a boat.

● Never provoke a shark, not even a small one, by spearing it, riding it, hanging onto its tail, or any other activity that might seem like a good idea at the time. Even a very small shark can inflict serious, possibly fatal, injuries.

Advice for victims

● Use any object to hand to fend off the shark, but try not to provoke it further.

● Remember that devices such as powerheads, gas guns, spearguns, and so on, have their limitations - do not expect them to accomplish the impossible. Such weapons, if used improperly, can incite a shark to attack rather than keep it at bay.

● Use available spears and knives to fend off the shark, and only attempt to wound it as a last resort.

● Be careful when making aggressive movements toward a shark. It may interpret these as a direct threat instead of being startled and swimming off.

● Once contact has been made or is imminent, fight the shark as best you can. Hit it with your bare hands only as a last resort. Probing its eyes and gills might force it away. Startling it by shouting or blowing bubbles could buy you valuable time.

● Most shark attacks produce wounds that are readily survivable. Bleeding should be controlled as quickly as possible, before the victim has been brought ashore.

The advice on these pages will not stop shark attacks occurring from time to time. It might not even significantly alter the number of shark attacks. But it might just save your life.

(Adapted from *Shark Attack* by David Baldridge)

INDEX

Page numbers in *italics* denote pictures